W9-AFL-559

plant biology today

advances & challenges

[

SECOND EDITION

plant biology today
advances & challenges

from symposia sponsored by the
american association for the advancement of science
and the botanical society of america

edited by

william a. jensen
leroy g. kavaljian

wadsworth publishing company, inc.
belmont, california

CONTENTS

PREFACE

Advances. Challenges. These words, which characterize modern science, ring out in virtually every report of current developments in chemistry, physics, and biology. In some ways, these words are most valid for the life sciences. Here the challenges are especially great; for the problems are difficult and profound, and the advances are as exciting as they are hard won. This volume presents a series of articles concerned with problems of immediate importance in the plant sciences—problems that illustrate graphically both the advances and challenges which are the very essence of current biological research.

Eleven topics are presented: (1) molecular botany, (2) the problem of cell development in plants, (3) photosynthesis, (4) biological clocks, (5) the movement of dissolved substances within plants, (6) the application of biochemistry to systematics, (7) the evolution of pteridophytes and gymnosperms, (8) electron transport in plants, (9) the organization and growth of lichens, (10) evolution in ferns, and (11) phytochrome and its role in plants. In each article the writer has attempted to give the reader background information and some knowledge of the most recent advances in the particular field. The problems discussed are currently under intensive investigation, with new data accumulating almost daily.

Each of the authors has worked in some area of the problem he discusses, and each is a recognized scientist who has added significantly to the area he is investigating. For these reasons a sense of excitement pervades all the articles as the data are discussed and new, unsolved problems are described. The life of the scientist in the laboratory revolves around the ever-present unsolved problem. Unfortunately, not all problems are solved nor all questions answered. Advances are made unevenly, and the research botanist encounters as many stone walls as he does breakthroughs.

This collection gives more than just a summary of old information and also more than just the recent advances. It reflects the growth and development of modern botany in the form of discussions of a variety of important problems.

Science can advance only as men recognize and rise to the challenges that exist. We hope that we have made some of these challenges as real and exciting to the reader as they are to us.

William A. Jensen

Leroy G. Kavaljian

plant biology today

advances & challenges

MOLECULAR BOTANY

1

James Bonner

Division of Biology
California Institute of Technology

Molecular botany comes to grips with how molecules interact to make the plant live. Molecular botany is concerned with where enzyme molecules come from, what genes are, and how genes cause a whole magnificent plant to be assembled. Unfortunately there are only a few molecular botanists practicing in the world today, so we do not yet know all about these matters. Nonetheless, we know something.

Molecular botany is concerned with the particles and structures inside of cells. All plant cells—and indeed all animal cells too—have very similar kinds of particles and structures swimming around in their insides. A plant cell on the average is perhaps 100 microns in diameter, and it is surrounded by a cell wall, more or less rigid, that provides the cell with a protective coat. Inside this carbohydrate cell wall is a membrane. The purpose of the membrane, a fatty structure, is to keep inside of the cell all of the things supposed to be there, but at the same time to let food molecules and water in. Within the membrane are the structures every botanist has seen through a microscope. These structures include, first of all, the nucleus. Every proper plant cell has a nucleus—generally one—and this is some 10 to 20 microns in diameter. In addition to the nucleus are the chloroplasts, if the cell is photosynthetic. The chloroplasts, perhaps fifty of them, are usually 5 to 10 microns in diameter—large enough to be seen in the light microscope. On the level of resolution of the light microscope may also be seen the numerous mitochondria; these are spherical or rod-shaped particles, a few microns in diameter and length, and perhaps 500 in number. With the electron microscope, botanists in the early 1950s were able to see in plant cells a still smaller type of particle not visible with the light microscope. This particle, some 20 millimicrons in diameter, has been named the ribosome. Ribosomes are extremely numerous; the typical plant cell contains some half-million of them. On a still smaller level of resolution may be seen the enzyme molecules. Enzyme molecules—some 2 millimicrons in diameter—are even more numerous than the ribosomes, and total perhaps 500 million per cell. On a still lower level of resolution, and as yet invisible in the plant cell by microscopy, one should find food molecules such as those of sugars recently photosynthesized, building blocks for making enzymes, as well as substances intermediate between recently synthesized food molecules and these same sugars.

All of these entities—nucleus, chloroplasts, mitochondria, ribosomes, enzymes, food, and metabolite molecules—make up the cytoplasm of the plant cell. The cytoplasm of the plant cell surrounds the central vacuole. This vacuole, composed of water, salts, tannins in some instances, and other small molecules, does not contain cytoplasm, but is merely a watery sort of waste sump for the cell.

One of the principal objectives of molecular botany has been to find out what each of these different kinds of particles contributes to the overall well-being of the cell. What does each contribute to life? This question is most easily answered by first separating the different kinds of subcellular objects in order to find out what each is made of and what each does. One of the great triumphs of molecular botany of the last ten years has been the development of simple methods to separate from one another all the kinds of subcellular plant structures. The molecular botanist grinds up some plant cells, a group of cells such as a tissue, or even a whole organ such as a root or a stem. By such grinding, the cell walls and membranes of each of the cells are torn. The molecular botanist then puts the ground tissue in a cheesecloth, or other readily available kind of bag, and squeezes it. The cell wall particles are sufficiently large so that they stay within the bag, but the juice squashed out contains the subcellular particles. We now have a suspension composed of all of the things inside cells. To separate these entities from one another, we put the suspension of subcellular particles into a centrifuge tube. We then spin the tube in the centrifuge so that the particles of the suspension are subjected to a sedimenting force of greater than one gravity, $1 \times g$. Under these conditions the biggest and heaviest objects in our suspension, the nuclei sediment first to the bottom of the centrifuge tube. After the nuclei have sedimented, the upper layer of solution—the supernatant, as it is called—can be decanted. The nuclei can be resuspended in water or other appropriate medium. We now have at our disposal a pure preparation of nuclei. The supernatant containing chloroplasts and smaller particles can be centrifuged again, using a slightly greater centrifugal force. The second-biggest and densest particles, the chloroplasts, sediment to the bottom. To sediment nuclei ordinarily requires 100 to 200 $\times$ g for 10 or 15 minutes. To sediment chloroplasts requires 1,000 to 2,000 $\times$ g for about 15 minutes. Once the chloroplasts have been removed, sedimentation of mitochondria requires centrifugation at about 10,000 $\times$ g for 15 minutes. The sedimentation of ribosomes requires still higher centrifugal forces—about 100,000 $\times$ g for one hour. In principle, the enzyme molecules, too, could be sedimented out in this same way by centrifugation. However, enzyme molecules are very small and the centrifugal forces required for their sedimentation would be very great. It is easier to separate enzymes by precipitation with ammonium sulfate and other chemicals. The point is that it is possible to separate each of the subcellular entities of the plant cell, and to collect representative portions of each in a fairly pure form.

We are now in a position to inquire what each type of subcellular particle is made of and what each does. Let us start with the enzyme molecules. There are, in a typical plant cell, about 10,000 different kinds of enzyme molecules. Since there are about 500 million enzyme molecules altogether in the cell, each cell contains about 50,000 representatives of each of the 10,000 kinds of enzyme molecules. There is an enzyme molecule to speed and catalyze every kind of chemical reaction in living things. An appropriate enzyme speeds each of the many kinds of chemical reactions required to transform available food molecules into the building blocks for making more cellular material. Since there are about 10,000 kinds of enzyme molecules in the typical plant cell, there are correspondingly about 10,000 kinds of enzyme reactions going on in that cell.

Each of the 10,000 different kinds of enzymes of the characteristic plant cell is a unique and specific kind of chemical compound, different from all other kinds of enzymes. All enzyme molecules belong to that great group of substances known as protein. A protein is, in essence, a long-chain molecule made of building blocks stapled together one after another. In a typical enzyme molecule this chain is about 150 building blocks long. The building blocks of which enzyme molecules are made are known as amino acid molecules; therefore in the typical enzyme about 150 amino acid molecules are stapled together to form the enzyme molecule. In plant cells, and indeed in all living things, there are twenty different kinds of amino acid building blocks. In all enzyme molecules the long chain of 150 amino acid building blocks is made of these same twenty different kinds of building blocks. The sequence in which the different species of building blocks succeed one another down the length of the chain will determine what kind of enzyme molecule the enzyme is. An enzyme molecule is a kind of message written in the twenty-letter alphabet of the amino acids. If we could understand the language of the twenty kinds of amino acids, the message in one enzyme molecule might read, "I am catalase, and it is my function to cleave H_2O_2 into oxygen and water." If one is making an enzyme molecule, one dare not make a mistake in the order in which one assembles the twenty different kinds of amino acid building blocks. One wrong building block inserted anywhere along the chain could produce an enzyme molecule inactive in carrying out the assigned reaction.

Where do enzyme molecules come from? They are not alive. One can take enzyme molecules and put them in a beaker and give them all of the goodies that enzyme molecules like, but they will not reproduce themselves. They do not multiply; they are made. Ribosomes synthesize enzyme molecules. Each ribosome possesses the power of synthesizing one particular kind of enzyme molecule. Since there are 10,000 kinds of enzyme molecules, and since there are 500,000 ribosomes in a typical cell, this means there are about fifty ribosomes for making each of the 10,000 kinds of enzyme molecules of the plant cell.

How do the ribosomes do their task? The assemblage of an enzyme molecule is obviously an information-requiring job. If one wishes to make an enzyme molecule, one has to have the recipe; one has to know the order in which to assemble the twenty different kinds of building blocks in the long chain that constitutes the particular kind of enzyme. Ribosomes use a long, printed tape containing instructions about how to make the desired enzyme molecule. The tape is composed of a series of information units. The first information unit on this tape says something like, "To read the information that I contain, please start here." (It is important not to start reading at the wrong end and get it all backward.) The second information unit says something like, "To make the enzyme for which I have information, please put amino acid of kind No. X (whatever is the right kind) here." The third information unit says something like, "To make this particular kind of enzyme for which I have information, please put amino acid of kind No. Y here." And so on. When the proper kinds of amino acid molecules are assembled along the long information-containing tape, still another enzyme comes along and zippers all of the amino acid building blocks together in a long chain, and the enzyme molecule is now fabricated. The molecule leaves the ribosome and goes into the cell to speed the appropriate chemical reaction. The ribosome is free to start assembling another molecule from the amino acid building blocks. On the average, by the time a molecular botanist comes along and grinds the plant cell up, each ribosome has fabricated something like 1,000 of the enzyme molecules for which it contains information.

The information-containing tape of the ribosome is made of ribonucleic acid (RNA). RNA is a long-chain molecule made of four different kinds of building blocks that succeed one another in many different combinations down the length of the tape. The tape is a "message" in the four-letter alphabet of RNA, telling the order in which to combine the twenty different kinds of amino acids, in order to assemble a specific kind of enzyme molecule. Since there are twenty different kinds of amino acids to be specified in the four-letter language of nucleic acid, the message-units in the tape that specify which kind of amino acid to put next must be several successive letters of the RNA alphabet. As a matter of fact, it is generally thought, although it has not been rigorously proved, that the message-units of the ribosomal tape are composed of three successive letters, since it takes at least three-letter words in a four-letter language to specify twenty different kinds of things, such as the twenty different kinds of amino acid building blocks. And so we can think of the ribosomal tape as a long message made of a series of three-letter words, each of these three-letter code words standing for one amino acid building block. The translation from the four-letter language of RNA to the twenty-letter language of amino acids, and therefore of enzymes, is known to biologists as coding. We are just beginning to be able to translate from RNA language to enzyme language. We know, for example, which three letters are contained in each of the three-letter code words that make up the ribosomal tape. We know which three RNA letters are contained in each of the twenty code words that stand for each of the twenty different kinds of amino acids. We also know the sequence in which the three letters succeed one another in each code word. It is therefore possible in principle to read the sequence of letters in an RNA molecule and state at once the amino acid sequence for which that RNA codes.

Where do the ribosomes and their RNA tapes come from? Ribosomes, like enzyme molecules, are not alive. They do not possess the power to multiply themselves. They hatch out enzyme molecules if supplied with the appropriate building blocks, but they are totally incapable of hatching out little ribosomes. Ribosomes are manufactured in the nucleus. We can say this because, in the first place, cells without nuclei cannot produce ribosomes. Some cells, such as those of the giant alga *Acetabularia,* can be enucleated easily. In *Acetabularia* the nucleus lurks conveniently in a rootlet or rhizoid at one end of the large cell. This rhizoid can be amputated without injury to the rest of the cell. The enucleated cell goes on making enzyme molecules, since it possesses ribosomes in plenty. It cannot, however, produce any more ribosome or any more information-containing RNA tapes. Contrariwise, isolated nuclei possess the power of making new ribosomes, when supplied with the building blocks for making ribonucleic acid.

Considerations of a still more general nature indicate that the RNA must obtain its information from the nucleus. It has been known to all botanists for many years that in the nucleus are to be found the chromosomes, each made up of many genes. We know, too, that the genes—the genetic material of the nucleus—contain the information that determines that the cell is a cell of a particular species of organism. The genes also contain information that specifies such things as flower color, leaf shape, etc. Through the work of George Wells Beadle and his colleagues—work begun over twenty years ago—it has been clearly shown that genes determine what kind of enzyme molecules the plant cell makes. In fact we say today, "One gene, one enzyme"—that is, one gene contains the information required to determine that that cell makes one kind of enzyme. A second gene contains information required to determine that the cell makes a second kind of enzyme, etc. We know this because a slight alteration (a mutation) in a gene causes a cell to make an altered, mutated enzyme molecule. Since we now know that enzyme molecules are made by ribosomes translating the information from RNA tapes, it is therefore clear that these entities must obtain their information content from the gene.

Before we can answer the question of how genes make ribosomal tapes, we must first consider that the genes are made of special gene material. This gene material is another kind of nucleic acid—deoxyribonucleic acid, or DNA, as it is known to all biologists. The genetic DNA is again a long-chain molecule made of four kinds of building blocks that can succeed one another down the chain in many combinations. Although it has not yet been rigorously proved, molecular botanists believe that the genetic information is contained in the sequence with which these building blocks of DNA succeed one another down the chain. The four kinds of building blocks of DNA resemble closely the four kinds of building blocks of RNA, with one specific and characteristic difference. The building blocks of DNA lack a particular oxygen-containing group found in the building blocks of RNA. This oxygen-containing group of RNA appears to be essential to enzyme formation. DNA does not, so far as we know today, possess the power to make enzyme molecules directly. This is reserved to RNA. However, the absence of the oxygen-containing group from the building blocks of DNA confers upon DNA a new and interesting property that RNA does not possess: DNA is able to multiply itself. DNA can replicate, conserving intact the information-containing sequence of building blocks, the sequence in which the genetic information is written.

DNA, as molecular botanists know, is composed of building blocks that may be symbolized by the names A, T, G, and C. The DNA chain is therefore made up of A, T, G, and C stapled together one after another. However, the DNA molecule is a double chain, not a single one. In this double chain there is a specific and characteristic relationship between the sequences of letters in the two strands. A basic selection rule at work—perhaps the most basic rule of biology—says that wherever there is an A in chain number 1, there must be a T in chain number 2. Where there is a G in chain number 1, there must be a C in chain number 2. A pairs with T; G with C. The two chains of the double-stranded DNA molecule fasten together tightly and firmly to form a uniquely coiled and stable structure, the DNA double helix. Biologists visualize the replication of DNA in the following terms. We imagine that when the DNA molecule wishes to replicate itself, it first comes unraveled at one end into two single strands. A supply of the building blocks A, T, G, and C is of course available in the nucleus for making more DNA. The two unraveled single strands of our DNA molecule now proceed to assemble upon themselves new mate chains from this pool of building blocks. In this assemblage, A pairs with T, G with C. The unraveling of the original double chain and the assemblage of new mate chains proceeds down the length of the original DNA molecule until we have two new double chains, each identical in structure with the original parent. Replication with conservation of information is the unique and wonderful property of DNA, making DNA the basic substance of life. DNA contains information, and it can replicate this information. DNA may be thought of as a do-it-yourself book containing all of the information about how to make a cell—and a do-it-yourself book that can multiply itself.

This view of how the DNA replicates itself has been established by many experiments. Among the most direct and easiest is to put some DNA into the test tube together with some of the building blocks, A, T, G, and C. After a short time, one finds twice the original amount of DNA. A little later, there is four times as much—and so on. DNA possesses the power to replicate itself, even in the test tube.

In the nucleus of the plant cell, the DNA molecules that are quite long are nonetheless not found as free DNA molecules. They are attached together in long strings and aggregates to form the chromosomes, each composed of many thousands or hundreds of thousands of individual DNA molecules, and the chromosome as a whole possesses the multiplicative property of the individual DNA molecules.

Let us now concern ourselves with how the information-containing RNA tape read by the ribosome is produced within the nucleus. This has been studied by molecular botanists in the most straightforward possible way. One isolates some nuclei, gives them the building blocks for making RNA, and looks to see whether RNA is made. It is. To determine more precisely where in the nucleus RNA is manufactured, a sensible and useful procedure is to grind up such isolated nuclei and to separate the subnuclear components, just as we earlier separated the subcellular components. Disrupted nuclei may be separated into nucleoli (the largest entity within the nucleus), the chromosomes, and—interestingly enough—nuclear ribosomes, the ribosomes contained within the nucleus. We may now incubate each of these different entities of the nucleus with the building blocks for making RNA, and see which part makes the RNA. We discover that the chromosomes make the RNA. The DNA of the chromosomes possesses the ability not only to multiply itself but also to print copies of itself in the form of RNA, when blocks for making RNA are present. These RNA copies of the genetic DNA constitute the ribosomal tapes and deliver and use the information about how to assemble the enzyme molecules of the cell. The RNA-containing tapes, after they are synthesized by the DNA, leave the nucleus—perhaps usually along with a ribosome that has in the meantime been synthesized in the nucleolus—and go out into the cytoplasm to undertake their chore of enzyme synthesis.

We can now begin to sense and feel the logic and strategy of the plant cell. It is the function of the plant cell, as it is indeed of all cells, to divide and make more cells, so that the individual can grow and the species increase in number. However, as all botanists know, before the cell can divide in two, it is first necessary that the chromosomes (genetic material) be doubled, so that at cell division each of the daughter cells may obtain a complete copy of the genetic information. The replication of DNA is the essential first step in the replication of the cell as a whole. If the DNA is to be replicated, the nucleus must have at its disposal a store of the building blocks A, T, G, and C. A, T, G, and C are not made directly by photosynthesis; sugars are produced by photosynthesis. All cells produce the A, T, G, and C necessary for the replication of the genetic material by enzymatic conversion of the available food into the appropriate building blocks. The DNA makes some RNA; the RNA, containing information about how to make enzymes, goes out into the cell in the form of a ribosome, and the ribosome assembles the enzyme for which it has information. A portion of the enzyme molecules thus assembled converts available food into amino acid building blocks for making more enzyme molecules. A further portion of the enzyme molecules is concerned with the reactions that convert the available food into building blocks for making more RNA, so that more ribosomes can be made to make more enzyme molecules. And finally, all of this complex machinery exists in the cell to provide enzyme molecules that convert a portion of the available food into the building blocks A, T, G, and C, so that these may be present in the nucleus, so that the DNA may replicate itself, so that the cell may divide in two, so that the creature may grow, and so that the species may multiply and cover the earth. This is the strategy of life. And in the operation of this cycle, we sense the principle of life itself. The DNA makes the RNA, the RNA makes enzymes, and the enzymes convert the food into building blocks for making all three. This picture of life as it is seen by molecular botanists is one that I like to refer to as the "Tricycle of Life."

We have in our discussion of the cell skipped over two important kinds of subcellular particles—the chloroplasts and the mitochondria—and we have done so for good reason. Chloroplasts, themselves contain their own genetic DNA, ribosomes, RNA tapes, and enzymes. The enzymes that the chloroplast makes are those required for photosynthesis, and indeed all of the photosynthetic machinery is present in the chloroplast. But many other kinds of metabolites essential to chloroplast growth are not made within it. Chloroplasts therefore live as symbionts in the cells of green plants, contributing photosynthesis to the overall welfare, but receiving from the host all needed building blocks for their own development. Chloroplasts, like other living cells, multiply by division and arise only from preexisting chloroplasts. Mitochondria, like chloroplasts, contain their own genetic DNA, make their own RNA and ribosomes and hence enzymes. It is the duty of the mitochondrial enzymes to conduct all of the reactions of respiration—the reactions by which food is burned with oxygen to form carbon dioxide and water, and in which a portion of the energy released is conserved in forms suitable for use in the energy-using reactions of the host cell. Like the chloroplast, the mitochondrion is dependent on its host cell for needed structural metabolites—for example, building blocks for DNA, RNA, and enzyme making. Like chloroplasts, mitochondria arise only by division of preexisting mitochondria and live as symbionts in the cells of higher organisms.

Molecular botany has thus obtained a moderately deep insight into the operation of the cell. There are still mysteries, to be sure, but the cellular mysteries appear soluble. Much more mysterious are the problems connected with assembling many cells into the structure of a multicellular organism. The plant begins its career as a fertilized egg, a single cell. This cell contains all of the genetic information about how to make the entire creature. The fertilized egg divides in two, each of these cells divides in two, and so on. Each daughter cell contains all of the genetic information that was contained within the fertilized egg. As embryonic cell division continues, the beginning of differentiation ultimately becomes apparent. Cells, even though they all contain the same genetic information, begin to differ from one another in appearance and in function. Most molecular botanists are agreed today that the differentiated and specialized cells of the higher organisms differ from one another in the kinds and amounts of the enzymes they contain. This difference in enzyme composition is the cause of differences in appearance and function of the different specialized cells of the adult organism. Even though the typical individual cell contains only perhaps 10,000 kinds of enzymes, the genetic material of the higher organisms contains information about how to make many more kinds of enzyme molecules—perhaps 30 to 100,000. That all of this genetic information is contained in each of the many kinds of specialized cells appears probable. For example, a differentiated and specialized cell may in some instances be encouraged to divide again, to de-differentiate, and to produce a bud and thence an entire plant. In such cases the specialized cell does, in fact, contain all the information about how to make the entire organism. And so, it would appear that in the individual cells of the higher organism, all of the genetic information is not used all of the time. It seems there must be present in the nucleus—in addition to information about how to make different kinds of enzyme molecules—further programming information about how to turn each bit of genetic information off and on in appropriate sequence and routine, to insure production of the varied kinds of specialized cells in the adult structure, all arranged appropriately. According to the surmises of molecular botany, this turning off and on of genetic information results in differentiation, the production of specialized cells, and the development of the entire adult plant.

A great deal of knowledge of how differentiation proceeds has been obtained at the anatomical and histological level. We know in the greatest detail about the embryology of plants, about the course of specialization of cells in meristems, and so on. But the basic mechanism of differentiation—the forces that bring about cell specialization—have remained *terra incognita*. However, the molecular botanist is coming close to being able to grapple with the problems of differentiation at the molecular level, which is the level on which the genes make the characteristic kinds of RNA. In this study of the molecular basis of differentiation lies the greatest future challenges to molecular botany.

REFERENCES

ASIMOV, I. *The Genetic Code*. New York: New American Library, Signet, 1962.

BLAKELY, L. M., AND F. C. STEWARD. "Growth and Organized Development of Cultured Cells, V: The Growth of Colonies from Free Cells on Nutrient Agar." *American Journal of Botany*, Vol. 51 (1964), pp. 780–791.

BONNER, J. *The Molecular Biology of Development*. New York: Oxford University Press, 1965.

————, R. C. HAUNG, AND R. V. GILDEN. "Chromosomally Directed Protein Synthesis." *Proceedings of National Academy of Science*, Vol. 50 (1963), pp. 893–900.

GIBOR, A., AND S. GRANICK. "Plastids and Mitochondria: Inheritable Systems." *Science*, Vol. 145 (1964), pp. 890–897.

HUANG, R. C., AND J. BONNER. "Histone, a Suppressor of Chromosomal RNA Synthesis." *Proceedings of National Academy of Science*, Vol. 48 (1962), pp. 1216–1222.

SALISBURY, F., AND R. V. PARKE. *Vascular Plants: Form and Function*. Belmont, Calif.: Wadsworth Publishing Co., Inc., 1964.

TUAN, Y. H., AND J. BONNER. "Dormancy Associated with Repression of Genetic Ac- *Plant Physiology*, Vol. 39 (1964), pp. 768–772.

THE PROBLEM OF CELL DEVELOPMENT IN PLANTS

2

William A. Jensen

Department of Botany
University of California, Berkeley

Many introductory botany courses begin with a discussion of the differences between plants and animals. The major point of such discussions is that there are differences between these groups—differences that make it meaningful to study plants as a unique group of organisms. Similarly, there are differences between plant and animal cells, and these differences present special problems when the development of these cells is examined.

The dissimilarities between plant and animal cells are not always immediately apparent to the observer. Frequently only an expert can identify an electron microscope photograph, showing just the cytoplasm of a cell, as part of a plant or animal cell. If, however, the photograph contains a portion of the wall, it is easily recognized as a plant cell. This difference demonstrates two points. First, plants and animals are in general enough alike so that we can expect many similar mechanisms to operate in the cell development and cell differentiation of both. Second, though similarities exist, there are also obvious differences between plant and animal cells—such as the presence in plant cells of large vacuoles and plastids—and thus we can speak of special problems of cell development in plants.

The most distinguishing characteristic of the plant cell is the presence of a rigid cell wall. This wall has the most profound implications, for it means that, in general, plant cells are stationary and hence cell migration plays no significant role in cell development. Therefore, because plant cells are immobile, the plane of cell division becomes the determining factor in cell development.

The presence of a wall also permits the formation of large cells, which attain their size by the growth of the wall. This growth occurs predominantly in one plane—that of the long axis of the cell—which results in elongation. However, many cells also undergo a period of radial enlargement, and in some, such as the derivatives of the cambium, wall growth occurs largely by radial enlargement.

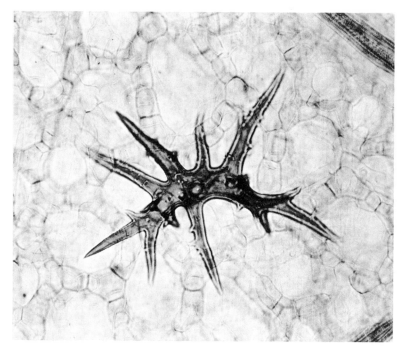

FIG. 2–1. Sclereid in the leaf of *Trochodendron aralioides*. [From A. S. Foster, "Plant Idioblasts: Remarkable Examples of Cell Specialization," *Protoplasma*, Vol. 46 (1956), p. 189. Reproduced by permission.]

In other cells such as sclereids, enlargement occurs in many directions (Fig. 2–1).

The unique and specialized character of the wall also is important in cell development. The nature of the wall distinguishes and defines the function of almost all types of plant cells—not only for vessel elements, fibers, and tracheids but also for many other types of plant cells.

The cell wall has been stressed here because it is one of the unique features of the plant cell and demonstrates the relationship that a single cell part may have to the course of cell development. A great deal of material is available to illustrate and study cell development in plants; however, we shall use the root tip, since it has been widely used in experimental studies. We shall consider a problem of cell development in roots, discussing first the general aspects and then as far as possible specific cell types and their development.

THE GENERAL COURSE OF CELL DEVELOPMENT

In 1875, the famous German botanist Carl Sachs studied root development by placing a series of ink marks on the surface of a root and then measuring the distances between these marks as the root grew. This classical experiment, known to all botanists and often performed as a laboratory exercise, demonstrates the general division of the growing root into zones of cell division, elongation, and maturation. In the first zone the cells divide; in the second they elongate; and in the third they mature. That this general picture of cell development is both correct and incorrect can be demonstrated in a number of ways. One method is to refine the original experiment by using a large number of ink spots and making a photographic record of their movement. This has been done in a very beautiful manner by Ralph Erickson of the University of Pennsylvania and his co-workers. A similar approach, carried out by Charlotte Avers of Rutgers University, is to make photomicrographs of the epidermis of the living root and follow the development of rows of cells. The general conclusions resulting from these studies are that the cells in the roots are undergoing some elongation at all points and that the rate of the elongation increases during the grand period of cell expansion. Similarly, cell divisions do not cease when the elongation increases, but continue for some distance up the root.

These and similar types of morphological and physiological analyses of root growth can form the basis for the chemical analysis of the root, which can then be interpreted in terms of cell development. It is clear from these analyses that cells develop in a relatively linear fashion, and that it is possible, at least in some ways, to treat the root as a homogeneous system. Thus, the analysis of sections by microchemical methods can yield information on chemical changes which accompany various stages of cell development.

This problem was originally approached by K. Linderstrom-Lang and Heinz Holter of the Carlsberg Laboratory in Copenhagen in their early work on barley-root tips, using special methods they had devised to analyze short segments of the root. These methods have evolved into a large body of procedures, termed quantitative histochemistry, which permit chemical analyses of very small segments of the root, frequently well below 100 microns in length. A specific example of this type of procedure is the measurement of ribonucleic acid (RNA) and deoxyribonucleic acid (DNA) in 100-micron segments of an onion-root tip. The root tips are first frozen at the temperature of liquid nitrogen, then dehydrated under vacuum and embedded in paraffin. No material is lost from the root during this process. The roots are then sectioned on a microtome, and the paraffin sections are placed in small tubes. The sections are now deparaffinized and the nucleic acids extracted by the standard acid-extraction procedure of using small micropipettes and microburettes to measure the volumes and to add and remove solutions. The absorption spectra of these solutions are then determined with the microattachment of a standard Beckman spectrophotometer. The cell number of the extracted section has been previously found; and, by simple division of the per-section value, the amount of RNA and DNA per cell in a 100-micron section can be calculated. In all of these procedures it is possible to run morphological controls which can be examined under the microscope, and the certainty of the position and condition of the cells extracted can be established.

The actual data collected in such a case can be seen in Fig. 2–2. Here the

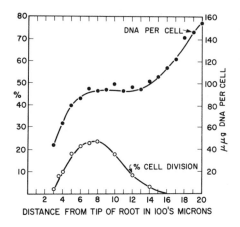

FIG. 2–2. The amount of DNA per cell as measured in consecutive 100-micron segments of the onion-root tip. Also plotted on the graph is the percentage of cell division per 100-micron segment. [From Jensen, Kavaljian, and S. Martinot, "The Incorporation of 3$_{\rm H-}$ thymidine by Developing Root Tip Cells," *Experimental Cell Research,* Vol. 20 (1960), p. 362. Reproduced by permission.]

data are plotted on a graph showing the amount per cell of nucleic acids plotted against the distance from the tip of the section analyzed. In this case 100-micron sections form the basis of the analyses. This type of graph indicates that the amount of DNA, for example, is low near the tip of the root and increases markedly during the early stages of cell development, reaches a small plateau as the cell begins to elongate, and then increases again with the rapid elongation of the cells. If we attempt to correlate these DNA data with cell-division data, we find that the first rise in DNA can be correlated with an increase in cell divisions as one moves back from the root tip. The second rise is actually correlated with a decrease in the number of division figures seen in the root as the cells begin to undergo elongation. This second rise indicates that the process of DNA synthesis, which at first is directly associated with cell division, becomes disassociated from cell division as the divisions cease and elongation begins. Essentially, these data tell us that DNA synthesis and the process of cell division can be divorced and that therefore we can have nuclei with higher amounts of DNA than would be expected normally. This very general phenomenon in plants is involved with the polyploidy, or increase in chromosome number, found in many plant nuclei. Polyploidy represents a doubling or increase in the chromosome number, which is not associated with subsequent cell division.

The same types of histochemical techniques can be used to analyze for various other cell components in addition to DNA. The amount of RNA and protein per cell can also be found with this type of method. In fact, one of the most successful of the techniques used by Linderstrom-Lang and Holter was a series of microkjeldahl determinations. These highly accurate determinations require only minute amounts of material and small amounts of equipment. Professor Linderstrom-Lang liked to give lectures in which he showed a match box containing what he termed his microkjeldahl apparatus, and it is indeed true that almost all the apparatus necessary for microkjeldahl determination, outside of a microburette, can be placed in a container no larger than a match box. If we examine the data (Fig. 2–3) that can be obtained from protein and nucleic

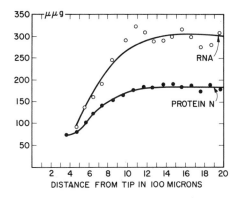

FIG. 2–3. The amount of RNA and protein per cell as measured in consecutive 100-micron segments of the onion-root tip. [From Jensen, "The Nucleic Acid and Protein Content of Root Tip Cells of *Vicia faba* and *Allium cepa*," *Experimental Cell Research*, Vol. 14 (1958), p. 578. Reproduced by permission.]

acid analyses, we find that they show some similarities to the DNA curve and some differences from it. Both RNA and protein increase per cell during the early stages of cell growth in the root; but when cell elongation begins, they level off for a considerable period. We know from other data—particularly that collected by Robert Brown in England, and Ralph Erickson and David Goddard in this country—that the amount of protein continues to increase beyond the area covered in this graph; nevertheless, it is interesting that for a short period at the beginning of elongation there is a leveling of the amount of RNA and protein per cell.

Cell-wall components can also be analyzed by means of quantitative histochemical procedures. We can extract the various cell-wall components from 100-micron sections and express the data obtained in relation to the various stages of cell development. This graph (Fig. 2–4) shows the change in cell-wall components during successive stages of cell development. The major conclusion from these analyses, based again on 100-micron sections of onion-root tips, is that all of the cells in the root contain all of the major wall components. These change in proportion, however, as the cell develops. We can see, for example,

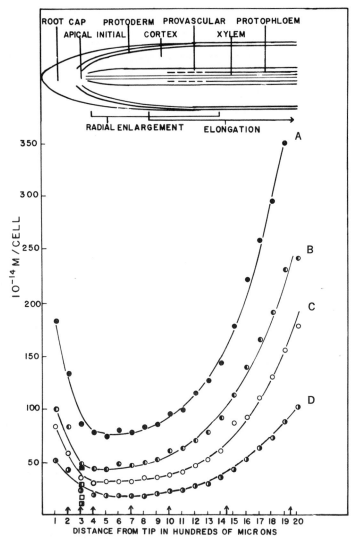

FIG. 2–4. The amount of the various wall components present in cells of the onion root at different stages of development. (A) Pectic substances; (B) hemicellulose; (C) noncellulosic polysaccharide; (D) cellulose. [From Jensen, "The Composition of the Developing Primary Wall in Onion Root Tip Cells: II, Cytochemical Localization," *American Journal of Botany,* Vol. 47 (1960), p. 292. Reproduced by permission.]

that the more insoluble parts of the wall—namely, the noncellulosic polysaccharides and the cellulose—increase markedly during the development of the wall. In addition, we can see that though the amount of material per cell increases markedly during cell elongation, the amount per unit surface area actually decreases as the cell passes through early stages of cell elongation. Later in the development of the cell there is a marked increase in the amount of cell-wall material, but for a time at the beginning of cell elongation there is a decrease in cell-wall material per unit surface area of the cell. The cell thus appears to be under some stress to form enough wall material to maintain its substantial rate of elongation.

We can list other types of knowledge that we have gained from this sort of analysis. For example, Robert Brown and his co-workers have been very diligent in studying the amount of various enzymes in larger segments, usually of ½ millimeter lengths, in bean roots. These data show a general pattern of enzyme content, which is low in the region just behind the root cap, increases markedly as the cells undergo elongation, and then drops off as cell elongation begins to cease.

PATTERNS OF TISSUE DEVELOPMENT

So far, all of the data we have considered can be collected and interpreted without examining the interior of the root. The root has been treated as an essentially homogeneous structure, in which the cells are all undergoing radial enlargement or division or cell elongation, although we realize that there is a great deal of overlap among these activities. If we now section the root and look at it morphologically, we find that we are dealing with anything but a homogeneous system. Rather, we are dealing with a remarkably complex system made up of numerous cell types and tissues (Fig. 2–5). We can see from these sections that the tip of the root consists of a special group of cells (the root cap), which surround and protect the apical initials. Behind the apical initials are the epidermis, the cortex, and the vascular tissues. The vascular tissue in turn can be broken down into many other tissues which begin their development fairly close to the tip; the metaxylem, for instance, extends almost to the area of the apical initials.

The question that immediately arises when one examines such sections is whether the data that have been collected on entire sections encompassing this vast array of cell types hold for each of the cell types making up the section. Another way of putting the question is "How much information have we lost by averaging different cell types in analyzing an entire section?" The quantitative histochemical data can form the background and the basis for more exhaustive studies of tissue and cell development.

Another set of histochemical procedures, generally called microscopic histo-chemical methods, permits the localization of materials within the cell. By com-bining the techniques of microscopic histochemistry with those of quantitative histochemistry, we can often gain an insight into the actual facts of cell develop-ment in a root. And if we are to understand what is governing, what is con-

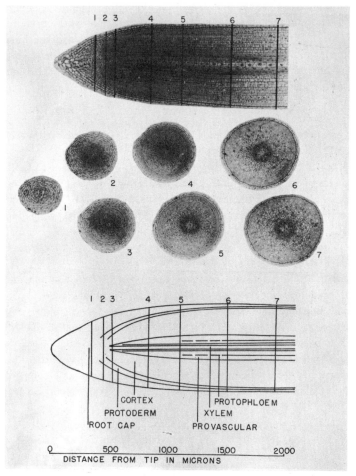

FIG. 2–5. The various tissues present in the tip of the onion root. The photograph of the root at the top corresponds to the diagram at the bottom. [From Jensen and Kavaljian, "An Analysis of Cell Morphology and the Periodicity of Division in the Root Tip of *Allium cepa*," *American Journal of Botany*, Vol. 45 (1958), p. 366. Reproduced by permission.]

trolling, what is directing the course of cell development, we must first understand what that course actually is in terms of the cells themselves and the tissues and organs they form.

Therefore, let us look at the nucleic acid and cell-wall picture, first with regard to the various tissues. There are a number of ways by which we can study the amount of DNA and RNA in the root, using microscopic histochemical procedures. DNA is easier to study and hence has been studied much more extensively than either RNA or protein. We can use the famous Feulgen reaction, which is a specific and quantitative color reaction for DNA. The color obtained from this reaction can be measured with a microspectrophotometer, and thus the relative amount of DNA per nucleus can be determined by this method. We can also use autoradiographic procedures, which permit the precise localization of radioactively labeled precursors that can be incorporated in the DNA of the nucleus. One of these precursors is thymidine, which is particularly useful because of its specificity for DNA. To obtain maximum resolution with the autoradiographs, we can use the radioactive isotope tritium as the labeled constituent of the thymidine molecule. Finally, to interpret the data collected by these methods, we must count the number of cell divisions that occur in the tissues of the root at selected distances from the tip.

If all these data are assembled in terms of the tissues present, some very interesting patterns emerge; these patterns are significantly different from those obtained by simply analyzing the entire sections. One of the most spectacular results of this type of analysis is the demonstration of the existence of a quiescent zone—a group of cells that are essentially nondividing. In other words, these are cells that either do not divide at all or that divide at a very slow rate, particularly those cells in the center of the quiescent zone. The quiescent zone, first described by F.A.L. Clowes in England, can be associated morphologically with the apical initials, which is a surprise to many morphologists. The apical initials in a wide range of roots have now been shown to be essentially nondividing or very slowly dividing cells. This is supported by the actual lack of division figures in this area and also by the lack of DNA synthesis, as shown by the lack of labeled nuclei when roots are presented with tritium-labeled thymidine (Figs. 2–6 and 2–7). The function of the quiescent center is by no

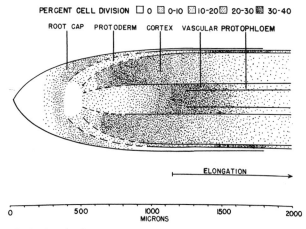

FIG. 2–6. The distribution of mitotic figures in the root showing the absence of divisions in the region of the apical meristems. [From Jensen and Kavaljian, *American Journal of Botany*, Vol. 45 (1958), p. 370. Reproduced by permission.]

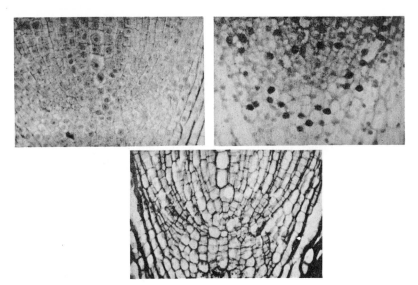

FIG. 2–7. The apical initials or quiescent center of the onion root.
Upper left: Microscopic preparation stained to show cellular detail.
Upper right: Autoradiograph of root grown in radioactive thymidine
which has been incorporated by nuclei synthesizing DNA. This
incorporation is visible by the concentration of dark silver grains
over the nuclei. Lower center: Cells stained to show only walls.

means clear, although we know through the work of Clowes that all the cells
divide during certain periods—particularly during the establishment of the secondary roots or after the root has been damaged. For the present it may be said
that the quiescent center functions as a reserve of cells that are less sensitive
to injury than the rest of the root and are able to restore growth of the root
once the growth has been stopped.

Cells divide immediately above and below the quiescent center—those below
giving rise to the root tip and those above forming the various tissues of the
root. Cell divisions are not as common above the apical initials as they are
farther up the root, and, as we have seen, the peak in number of cell divisions
comes about 1 millimeter from the tip of an onion root. In addition, the region
where a peak in the number of divisions occurs varies from one tissue to another.
Generally, in the vascular tissues the number of divisions in the xylem reaches
a peak very close to the tip; other types of vascular cells show a maximum
number of divisions farther up the root. On the whole, the epidermis in most
species also reaches a peak in number of cell divisions fairly close to the tip,
closer to the tip than to the cells of the cortex. If we now examine the amount
of DNA per cell and the incorporation pattern of thymidine into DNA in the
various tissues, we find that the general pattern established on the basis of the
analysis of entire 100-micron sections does not hold for all of the tissues con-

sidered individually. The cortex does follow the general pattern—which is not surprising, since the majority of cells in the root are cortical. The epidermis and vascular cells, however, provide two significant variations. In the epidermis the amount of incorporation and the amount of DNA increase as the number of cells in division increases. As the first plateau is reached, the amount of DNA and the amount of DNA synthesis remain constant in the epidermis—in contrast to the cortex, in which they continue to rise. Thus, our conclusion that DNA synthesis can be associated first with the increase in number of divisions and then with the beginning of elongation, or the cessation of divisions, holds only for the cortex and not for the epidermis. In the vascular tissue the converse case is true. Here the amount of incorporation and the amount of DNA increase substantially very close to the tip and out of phase with division, being higher than one would expect from the number of mitotic figures present.

It can be seen on the basis of these observations alone that one of the major problems concerning cell development in plants is the relation of this DNA increase, unrelated to cell division, to the development of a cell. At present it is probably best to assume that there is no direct relationship between this increase in DNA and the direction of the pattern of cell development, but that some common factor is influencing both elongation and DNA production in these tissues. It is, however, one of the several intriguing problems that arise when we consider nucleic acid metabolism in relation to the development of the cell. Another is the relation of this DNA increase and chromosome polyploidy to the formation of secondary roots and to the totipotency of the cells. Considerable evidence amassed by John Torrey of Harvard University indicates that cells with high DNA and polyploid levels are not those that give rise to secondary roots and to calluses in tissue culture. Torrey has also been able to show that kinetin appears to work in these areas as a specific stimulant in the division of polyploid cells. These problems, however, must be explored in greater depth in the future.

When autoradiographic procedures are used to study RNA and protein synthesis in the various tissues, we find again that differences exist between them. The apical initials appear to be inactive in synthesizing both RNA and protein. A steady but constant rate of synthesis goes on during the phases of radial enlargement, until the point is reached where the plateau per cell (Fig. 2–8) occurred in the other quantitative analyses discussed. At this point, which corresponds with the beginning of cell elongation, the amount of RNA and protein precursors incorporated increases tremendously, and we find a very marked change in the metabolic activity of the cell. It would seem that this increase represents a compensatory effect in synthesis and breakdown, which establishes a constant amount of RNA and protein per cell but in far different way than we might assume from the quantitative data. This change in metabolic activity at the beginning of rapid elongation in these cells is another area requiring attention in our study of cell development. How much this change

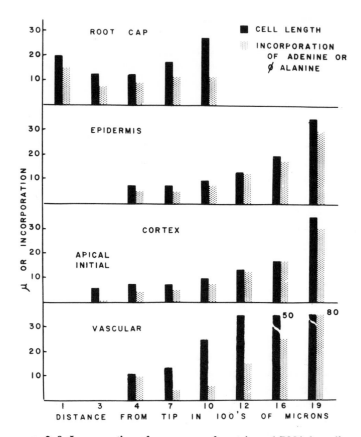

FIG. 2–8. Incorporation of precursors of protein and RNA by cells at various distances from the tip of the root. Also shown is the length of the cells. [From Jensen, "Relation of Primary Cell Wall Formation to Cell Development in Plants," in *Synthesis of Molecular and Cellular Structure,* edited for the Society for the Study of Development and Growth by Dorothea Rudnick. Copyright 1961, The Ronald Press Company.]

in metabolic rate is associated with the rapid formation of cell-wall components is unknown, but it is certainly one of the areas that should be examined in much greater detail.

Differences in cell-wall composition among the various tissues occur and provide another area for the study of patterns of tissue development. It is possible to demonstrate marked differences in cell-wall composition in mature cells, but this is not so easy in immature primary walls because the walls are thin and we lack definite color reactions that are specific for the wall components. We can get around this difficulty, however, by using a reaction that stains all the cell-wall parts. Then, using a system of differential extractions, we can, by inference, obtain a considerable amount of information concerning the composition of the developing primary wall.

The results of this type of analysis, which incorporates the data learned from quantitative histochemical determinations and from microscopic histochemical work, are shown in Fig. 2–9. Here we can see the changing composition of the

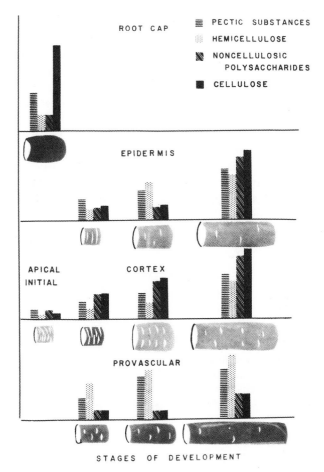

FIG. 2–9. The composition of the wall of tissues present in the root tip at various stages of development. [From Jensen in *Synthesis of Molecular and Cellular Structure,* 1961. Reproduced by permission of The Ronald Press Company.]

cell walls of the various tissues of the root as they undergo the early stages of their development. Figure 2–9 shows that the apical initials are very low in all cell-wall components, but that all cell-wall parts are present. The cortex follows the pattern established for the generalized cell on the basis of quantitative histochemical work. The cortical cells in the very early stages of growth are relatively low in such components as the pectic substances and hemicellulose. Both the pectic substances and the hemicellulose increase as the cell elongates. In all stages of development the cortical cells are relatively high in the noncellulosic polysaccharides and cellulose. This same general pattern holds for the epidermis, except that those epidermal cells that are in the phase of radial enlargement and early elongation are very high in pectic substances and hemicellulose. During this period of growth, the root cap no longer completely surrounds the exterior of the root, and the epidermis develops a heavy outer cell wall. This heavy outer cell wall appears particularly rich in pectic substances and in hemicellulose. The epidermal cells synthesize a considerable amount of noncellulosic polysaccharides and cellulose during early elongation and thus balance the picture, so that the proportion of the relatively soluble versus the relatively insoluble wall components is much closer to that found in the cortex. This pattern of high, relatively soluble wall components during the early stages of cell development is even more marked in the provascular tissue. Here both pectic substances and hemicellulose are very high during almost all stages of development, and the corresponding insoluble components, noncellulosic polysaccharides and cellulose, are low. These differences in cell-wall composition occur very early in the development of the cell, and the mechanism and control of their formation need to be investigated thoroughly.

DEVELOPMENT OF SPECIFIC CELL TYPES

Let us continue by examining in more detail the development of the vascular tissue. In most roots the vascular tissue develops quite close to the tip. In the onion, which we have been using most extensively, the development of the metaxylem occurs very close to the apical initials, while the development of other elements of the xylem occurs farther up the root. The formation of the phloem takes place about a millimeter from the tip. The xylem elements will eventually form heavy cell walls, one of the major features of xylem development being the formation of lignin in the walls. Of interest is the fact that in the provascular tissue, which gives rise to the xylem and other vascular cells, the noncellulosic polysaccharides and the cellulose components of the wall are low. Thus it would seem that where lignification is not a major aspect of cell development, as in the cortex, the more substantial structural elements of the cell wall (the noncellulosic polysaccharides and cellulose) are more heavily represented. In the xylem, however, these components are poorly represented in the early stages of development; and as maturation begins, the formation of lignin is imposed on the system.

Several years ago, I examined in the root tips of *Vicia faba* the possibility of inducing or increasing peroxidase activity by adding indolacetic acid. With this addition, the elements of the vascular tissue, particularly the xylem that will form lignin, showed the capacity to increase the amount of peroxidase activity present in the cells. Work by Sanford Siegel and others has indicated that peroxidase or similar enzymes are involved in certain stages of lignin formation; knowing this, we may perhaps begin to understand some of the complexities of the problem of cell development in a specific cell type. It may be that in the formation of the xylem a series of metabolic changes takes place, resulting in a cell low in noncellulosic polysaccharides and cellulose. These changes are then followed by a series of subsequent modifications involving an increase in peroxidase activity, regulated by the presence of indolacetic acid. This peroxidase activity is associated with the production of a lignified cell wall. The question of how all these steps are actually integrated and what constitutes the controlling mechanism is one of the truly basic problems in our understanding of cell differentiation and development in plants—not only in terms of glittering generalities about the role of DNA and RNA but in specific pathways leading to exact and known end results.

Still another example illustrates well the complications in the sequence of events leading to the formation of a specific cell type. This is the work of Charlotte Avers on the formation of root hairs. Her investigation began with a careful analysis of the rate of cell formation in the epidermis of grass roots. She was able to demonstrate that, at a very early stage of cell development when the cells are still elongating very slowly, there is a significant difference in the rate of development between the cells that will form root hairs and those that will not. We are first able to tell which cells will form root hairs and which will not when we can observe an unequal cell division—by unequal, we mean that one of the daughter cells is smaller than its sister. (This is one of many instances of cell division characterizing the origin of a specific cell type.) Dr. Avers was able to show very clearly that shortly after the formation of the two daughter cells there is a difference in their rate of elongation. But this difference in rate of elongation, which occurs quite awhile before the actual formation of the root hair by the cell destined to form it, lasts only a short time and then both cells elongate at relatively the same rate. Dr. Avers was also able to apply a series of microscopic histochemical procedures that demonstrated striking enzymatic differences between the cells (Fig. 2–10). The difference in cytochrome oxidase content is very apparent. She also discovered differences in succinic dehydrogenase and acid phosphatase activity. Thus it would seem that early in the history of the cell that will form the root hair a substantial change takes place, which is reflected both in the rate of elongation and in the enzymatic activity of the cell. These differences seem to follow very shortly after an unequal cell division—a cell division that gives rise to what may be called an energetic cell and a less- or nonenergetic cell. The energetic cell, which will form a root hair, shows substantially different enzymatic activity, thus indicating that the cell will form a new cell type.

FIG. 2–10. Distribution of cytochrome oxidase in cells that produce root hairs (short cells) and those that do not (long cells). [From C. J. Avers, "Histochemical Localization of Enzyme Activity in the Root Epidermis of *Phleum pratense*," *American Journal of Botany*, Vol. 45 (1958), p. 612. Reproduced by permission.]

SOME GENERAL CONCLUSIONS

From this brief summary of some of the aspects of cell development that can be observed in one part of a higher plant—namely, the root tip—it is clear that we still need a great deal of biochemical and morphological evidence before we will be able to define in meaningful terms the course of cell development in plants. What we are faced with at present is a great void between, on the one hand, an expanding body of knowledge about nucleic acid and genetic factors, and, on the other, a fully developed cell with all its intricacies and mysteries. We know a great deal about the action of growth substances on cell elongation and some things about growth substances in relation to the stimulation of cell division; but we know virtually nothing about the course of the formation of perhaps the most characteristic part of the plant cell—its wall. Furthermore, we understand little about those factors that determine the plane of cell division in plants, which is so critical in the maintenance of the form of the organ and in the origin of specific cell types. The importance of unequal cell division and the immediate biochemical differentiation that occurs in the unequal daughter cells must never be overlooked. All these are problems for which the parameters are at present indistinctly known, but which in the next decade may prove to be the vital problems of plant-cell research.

Colored Lights, Colored Plants

Jan Ingen-Housz, one of the earliest students of photosynthesis, observed that only green parts of plants can carry on this process. After the green pigments of plants were found to be the chlorophylls, it was natural to conclude that these were the active pigments in photosynthesis.

Better and more direct evidence was available after the colors of light used in photosynthesis (action spectrum for photosynthesis) were found to correspond to the light absorbed by the chlorophylls (that is, the absorption spectrum of the chlorophylls) in green algae. These algae, of which *Spirogyra* is an example, contain the same kinds of pigments—chlorophylls *a* and *b* and the yellow carotenoids—in the same relative amounts as do the green parts of higher plants. Engelmann's experiments conducted in the 1880s were elegant and simple. He placed a filament of a green alga on a microscope slide and bathed it in a suspension of oxygen-requiring motile bacteria. The slide was then placed on the stage of the microscope. Next, instead of illuminating the algal strand with white light, he interposed a prism between the light source and the microscope stage. In this way one end of the algal filament was illuminated with blue light, the other end with red light, and the region between with the other colors of the visible spectrum. Engelmann then counted the number of motile bacteria around each segment of the illuminated alga. This provided him with an estimate of the relative rate of oxygen production—and consequently of photosynthesis— of sections of the algal filament irradiated with different qualities of light. The largest number of bacteria surrounded those parts of the algal filament that were in blue light or red light. Of all the pigments present in the alga, chlorophylls alone absorbed both blue and red light. Since only light which is absorbed can be used, Engelmann concluded that the chlorophylls are the active photoreceptive pigments for photosynthesis.

During the past eighty years these conclusions have been confirmed repeatedly by investigators using a number of more refined techniques. In many of the newer devices, the principle is the same as that used by Engelmann: photosynthetic activity is measured by observing oxygen evolution. The differences are in the way in which the measurements are made. For example, suspensions of algae have been illuminated with different wavelengths of light and the amount of oxygen released has been measured physically, by volume, instead of biologically as with Engelmann's bacteria. Similar experiments have been done in which the oxygen evolved has been measured with a platinum electrode—a device with which oxygen can be measured electrically. The greatest refinement of these techniques for determining the action spectrum for photosynthesis has come in C. S. French's modification of a manual device used by Lawrence Blinks and Francis Haxo. French's machine uses a platinum electrode to measure oxygen release but is fully automatic in that the algae are successively illuminated with different wavelengths of light while oxygen evolution is simultaneously recorded

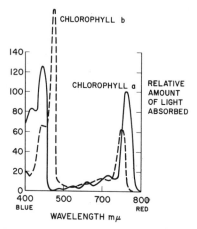

FIG. 3–1. Absorption spectra of chlorophylls *a* and *b*. These curves show that a solution of chlorophyll in either absorbs blue and red light but relatively little of other colors of light. Data of this sort are obtained with a *spectrophotometer.* A solution of a pigment is illuminated with a single wavelength of light (or really a small segment of the total spectrum), and the percentage of the incident light absorbed by the colored compound is measured with a photo cell. The "absorption spectrum" is obtained by repeating such measurements at points throughout the spectrum of visible light. Similar observations can be made in other regions—for example, the ultraviolet or infrared ranges. [From M. B. Allen, C. S. French, and J. S. Brown, "Native and Extractable Forms of Chlorophyll in Various Algal Groups," *Symposium on Comparative Biology,* Vol. 1 (1960), p. 34. Reproduced by permission.]

as a function of light quality. With a device of this sort, one can obtain relatively quickly the action spectrum for photosynthesis of the organism being studied (Fig. 3–1).

Studies with devices more refined than Engelmann's also revealed that chlorophyll *a* can be considered the main photosynthetic pigment, while other chlorophylls, and also certain additional pigments, may play cooperative roles not yet completely defined. Blue-green and red algae contain a single chlorophyll, chlorophyll *a;* the red and blue complexes of protein with bile pigments are the principal cooperating or "accessory pigments" in these organisms. (Mammals produce bile pigments in the breakdown of hemoglobin. These pigments, free of protein, are excreted in the feces.) Photosynthetic bacteria contain distinctive chlorophylls, but among the algae and high plants no case is known in which photosynthesis proceeds in the absence of chlorophyll *a.*

Carbon Dioxide and Light Intensity

The normal level of carbon dioxide in the earth's atmosphere today is about 0.04 percent. The photosynthetic apparatus in some modern plants appears to be "over-engineered" when the capacity for consuming carbon dioxide is compared with the natural abundance of this gas. Many algae grow better in concentrations of carbon dioxide more than a hundred-fold higher than its natural abundance. Photosynthesis by some crop plants in short-term experiments increases linearly with increasing carbon dioxide concentrations up to about 0.5 percent, roughly ten times the normal level of the gas in the atmosphere.

In contrast, the capacity of the photosynthetic apparatus to utilize light sometimes appears to be "under-engineered" for natural conditions. Full summer sunlight in many places on earth is in the neighborhood of 10,000 to 12,000 footcandles; yet the photosynthetic capacity of many plants is saturated at much lower intensities. However, these saturation data are for plants growing in the normal atmosphere containing 0.04 percent carbon dioxide. Some plants could utilize more of the light energy impinging on them if they were grown in concentrations of carbon dioxide higher than normal.

In natural environments does the availability of carbon dioxide or of light restrict the extent to which a plant's photosynthetic capacity is utilized? In many cases the level of carbon dioxide in the atmosphere restricts photosynthesis; on the other hand, the photosynthetic rates of some mosses and algae, as well as numerous "shade" plants growing in caves or under very heavy foliage, may be limited primarily by light intensity. The full photosynthetic capacity of an organism is seldom realized in nature. Green organisms in large numbers seem to be looking forward to a universal plenty of carbon dioxide—to which we mammals would find it difficult to adjust; yet the plants themselves work vigorously to use up the carbon dioxide around them.

The concentration of carbon dioxide in the atmosphere is fairly constant at all points on earth, although minor variations can exist in a plant's microclimate. Light, on the other hand, is something for which plants have competed. Some species have adapted by developing costly, tall superstructures upon which to display photosynthetic organs to the sun; others, by trimming their metabolic demands so as to be able to accept a permanent place in the shade.

The minimum light intensity in which a plant can survive but not grow appreciably—that is, at which its photosynthetic activity just balances its respiratory losses—is its physiological compensation point. Each plant species has established a minimum standard for life; each member of the species achieves this or perishes. Compensation points for plants range from perhaps 2 up to 100 footcandles or more. The compensation point for a single leaf of field-grown corn is about 100 footcandles at 30°C. It is obvious that one factor that may determine the distribution of a species may be its compensation.

Water

Water uptake and water loss are extremely serious problems for the survival of higher land plants; the solutions that have evolved are all compromises. Water is one of the reactants in photosynthesis. Yet if one counts the total amount of water absorbed by a corn plant and also measures the amount of water it

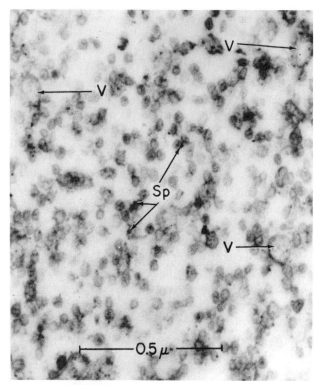

FIG. 3–3. An electron micrograph of a thin section of a typical chromatophore preparation. The chromatophores occur singly, in clumps, and occasionally as chains. This aggregation seems to be produced by the fixative. Larger vesicles (V) may be present. It is not known whether or not these structures are large chromatophores. Small dense particles (Sp) are often present as contaminants. Magnification ×78,000. [From Bergeron and Fuller, in *Macromolecular Complexes*, 1961. Reproduced by permission of The Ronald Press Company.]

Quanta, Electrons, Atoms, and Molecules

We have proceeded from a consideration of photosynthesis in the intact plant down to the fine structure of the photosynthetic apparatus as revealed in the electron microscope. Continuing from a new point of view, let us examine photosynthesis at the level of quanta of light, electrons, atoms, and molecules. It is from such examinations that the most rapid and startling changes in our concept of photosynthesis have come in recent years. We hope that these ideas will at some time be related to the kinds of things we can see in the electron microscope

Cornelis van Niel re-examined the classical formula about thirty years ago and clearly perceived that part of photosynthesis is "just" another biological

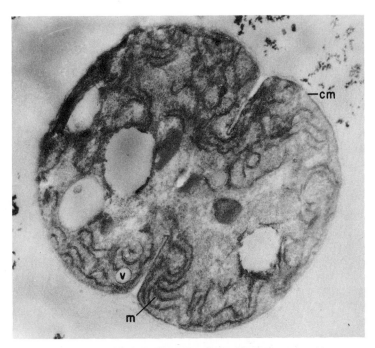

FIG. 3–4. Two cells in a filament of the blue-green alga *Nostoc.*
The protoplast is enclosed by a cell membrane (cm) and is differentiated into an outer region and an inner region. Numerous photosynthetic membranes (m) are scattered throughout the outer region which also contains a number of membrane-enclosed vacuoles (v). Magnification ✕40,000. [From F. V. Mercer, L. Bogorad, and R. Mullens, "Studies with *Cyanidium calderium:* I, The Fine Structure and Systematic Position of the Organism," *Journal of Cell Biology,* Vol. 13 (1962), p. 393.]

electron-transferring, or oxidation-reduction, process and that one can conceive of photosynthesis as consisting of two distinct but interlocked segments. One part is the fixation of the carbon of atmospheric carbon dioxide and its reduction— that is, acceptance of electrons—to raise it to the higher energy level of a carbohydrate. This has come to be called the "path of carbon" in photosynthesis. The second segment, according to this modern view, is the generation, at the expense of light energy, of the materials which can be used by the cell to drive this reduction.

The release of oxygen by photosynthesizing plants is associated with the second segment, which has been called the photolysis of water. It was visualized (Fig. 3–8) as a splitting of water at the expense of light energy into a highly reducing —that is, a strong electron donor—component [H], and a strong oxidant or electron acceptor [OH]. (These are not the ions H+ and OH-- but, as the brackets

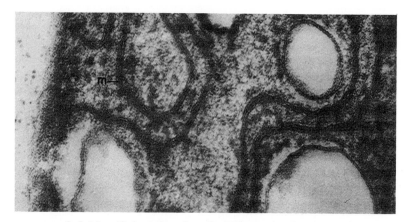

FIG. 3–5. Magnified portion of a cell of *Nostoc* showing the multiple layers of the photosynthetic membranes (m). Magnification ×130,000. [From Mercer, Bogorad, and Mullens, *Journal of Cell Biology*, Vol. 13 (1962), p. 393. Reproduced by permission.]

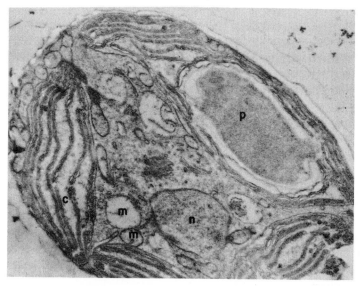

FIG. 3–6. Mature cell of the green alga *Chlorella pyrenoidosa* as viewed in the electron microscope. The nucleus (n), mitochondria (m), and the chloroplast (c) with its pyrenoid (p) are visible. In green algae, the photosynthetic membranes of the chloroplast are surrounded by a conspicuous membrane. Magnification ×40,000. [From Mercer, Bogorad, and Mullens, *Journal of Cell Biology*, Vol. 13 (1962), p. 393. Reproduced by permission.]

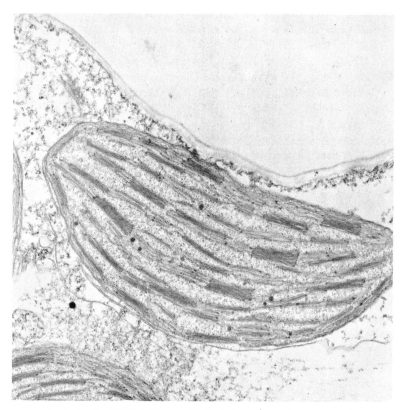

FIG. 3–7. A 46,000-fold magnified picture of a thin section of a chloroplast from a corn leaf. Notice the conspicuous membrane around the chloroplast as well as the layering of the photosynthetic membranes into stacks called "grana." [Through the courtesy of Ann Jacobson, Department of Botany, University of Chicago.]

intend to denote, highly reactive radicals. [H] is composed of an electron, $e-$, plus a hydrogen ion or proton, $H+$.) A later discussion will consider the possibility, being discussed among many students of this problem today, that water-splitting may well summarize this segment of photosynthesis but that the reducing component may in fact be generated in a somewhat different way.

Robin Hill's demonstration in 1934 that isolated chloroplasts can release oxygen when illuminated in the presence of a hydrogen acceptor was striking proof that photosynthesis can be *experimentally* separated into two parts (Fig. 3–9). The experiments of Ruben and Kamen also supported Van Niel's contention. In these experiments illuminated green algae were supplied with CO_2^{18} plus H_2O^{16} or with CO_2^{16} plus H_2O^{18}. When the oxygen produced during photosynthesis was collected and analyzed, it was clear that it arose not from carbon dioxide but from water.

$$\text{\textit{Light-requiring} \atop \textit{process:}} \quad \begin{bmatrix} X + Y \\ HOH \end{bmatrix} \xrightarrow{\;Lt\;} \begin{bmatrix} X \\ H \end{bmatrix} + \begin{bmatrix} Y \\ OH \end{bmatrix} \qquad A$$

Processes not
requiring $XH \xrightarrow{\hspace{1.5cm}} Synthetic\ reactions$ B
light energy: $YOH + YOH \rightarrow Y + Y + H_2O + \frac{1}{2}O_2$ C

FIG. 3–8. X and Y represent hypothetical acceptors for the two fission products of water. The concept of such acceptors was introduced into thinking about photosynthesis because the two products [H] and [OH] would tend to have a very high affinity for one another—that is, they would be expected to react readily with one another unless each is "tied" to some acceptor. (A) The photolysis of water. (B) The link between the photolysis of water and the path of carbon. (C) The oxygen release process.

The Path of Carbon

The path of carbon in photosynthesis is today the more clearly defined of Van Niel's two segments. Let us examine this first and later look at photosynthesis on the level of photons, electrons, and atoms.

$$4HOH + Acceptor \xrightarrow[\text{\textit{Chloroplasts}}]{\textit{Lt}} 2H_2O + O_2 + [H]\ Acceptor$$

FIG. 3–9. Robin Hill discovered that suspensions of chloroplasts, prepared from leaves, could produce oxygen when illuminated *provided* the suspension contained a compound, such as an $Fe+++$ salt, which could accept electrons—that is could be reduced. This reaction is in accord with Van Niel's idea that photosynthesis is an oxidation-reduction reaction: HOH is an electron or hydrogen donor that is oxidized (an electron plus a proton is removed). During photosynthesis, in contrast to the Hill reaction, carbon in phosphoglyceric acid is the ultimate hydrogen acceptor—that is, it is reduced.

We know from the equation $6CO_2 + 6H_2O \xrightarrow{\hspace{1.5cm}} C_6H_{12}O_6 + 6O_2$ that carbon goes into the plant (and ultimately into the chloroplast) as carbon dioxide and comes out as carbon at the level of a carbohydrate—for example, as part of a sugar like glucose. What are the intermediate compounds? What are the mechanisms of the reactions involved?

Before about 1946, in investigations of this problem using microanalytical methods, it was possible to compare the carbon compounds in the leaf only before and after one-half hour or more of photosynthesis. Practically all of the carbon dioxide could be accounted for as glucose or more complex carbohydrates. These data supported some observations made by Boussingault in 1864 but provided no clues to the mechanisms by which sugars were formed. Then, in the late 1940s, the long-lived radioactive isotope of carbon, carbon-14, became available and was used in a series of masterful experiments which led to an understanding of the path of carbon in photosynthesis.

In these experiments, suspensions of algae were supplied with carbon dioxide, labeled with carbon-14. After periods of photosynthesis ranging from 0.3 of a second to longer intervals, the cells were killed quickly. Newly formed compounds contained radiocarbon and thus could be detected in minute amounts in extracts of the algae. The relatively new technique of paper chromatography was used to separate the components of each extract. The compounds containing radioactive carbon were then detected by radio-autography. In this technique, a paper chromatogram is placed next to a sheet of photographic film in the dark; then the beta particles emitted by the decaying atoms of carbon-14 act like particles of visible radiation in the way they affect the photo-sensitive emulsion. When the film is developed and compared with the paper chromatogram, the labeled compounds produced during photosynthesis can be located easily.

The research group at the University of California at Berkeley, led by Melvin Calvin and Andrew Benson, used these procedures. They studied extracts of cultures of the green algae *Chlorella* and *Scenedesmus,* which had been permitted to carry on photosynthesis for various lengths of time. They concluded that radiocarbon from $C^{14}O_2$ appears first in the three-carbon compound, phosphoglyceric acid; next, in phosphoglyceraldehyde, which is a phosphorus-containing sugar; then later, in a large number of other carbohydrates, amino acids, and other types of compounds. Radioactive sugars were disassembled, carbon atom by carbon atom, and the precise location of the labeled atom in each compound was established. A path of carbon in photosynthesis from carbon dioxide to many well-known constituents of the cell could then be written with confidence. The Nobel Prize in Chemistry for 1961 was awarded to Calvin for this work.

Still, at this stage, one major piece of information was lacking. The $-COOH$ group of phosphoglyceric acid comes from carbon dioxide, but what compound in the cell contributes the other two carbon atoms of this three-carbon organic acid? What compound is the acceptor for carbon dioxide? This problem was solved with the unexpected discovery that a five-carbon sugar containing two atoms of phosphorus, ribulose diphosphate, combines with carbon dioxide; and, from this six-carbon compound, two three-carbon molecules of phosphoglyceric acid are produced. Only one of the two molecules of phosphoglyceric acid contains radio-carbon if the algae have been provided with $C^{14}O_2$, but they are otherwise identical and the photosynthesizing organism can hardly distinguish between them. Some key compounds on the path of carbon in photosynthesis are shown in Fig. 3–10. The processes outlined can be divided into three phases; first, carbon dioxide fixation; second, the reduction of phosphoglyceric acid to the carbohydrate phosphoglyceraldehyde; finally, a large number of reactions, which can be grouped under the heading "carbohydrate interconversions." One course included among these latter transformations is the formation of additional ribulose diphosphate. The steps outlined in Fig. 3–10 are thus part of a cycle; in fact, many cycles could be added to this summary.

Is all of this photosynthesis? As we learn more about photosynthesis, it seems to become increasingly difficult to define the term. We could say that the production of phosphoglyceraldehyde is a terminal reaction in photosynthesis. However, it would also be accurate to say that the addition of electrons to phosphoglyceric acid (that is, its reduction to phosphoglyceraldehyde), which requires a great deal of energy, is the only photosynthetic step in the path of carbon. In photosynthesis, the reduction of phosphoglyceric acid to phosphoglyceraldehyde is at the junction of the energy-electron path and the path of carbon.

Photons and the Path of Electrons

The path of electrons begins almost simultaneously with the absorption of a quantum of light by a molecule of chlorophyll and, in the sense we will use it here, ends with the utilization, in the reduction of the organic acid to the carbohydrate, of materials produced as a consequence of light absorption.

Before we approach the junction of the paths of carbon and energy from another route (when we will enter photosynthesis with a photon of light), it is profitable to examine this junction more closely. This examination should help us recognize some landmarks when we approach the juncture of these two paths again but from another direction. As we move back and forth through this junction, between the landmarks of phosphoglyceric acid and phosphoglyceraldehyde, it will become a familiar place. The conversion of the acid to the sugar is reversible and was known to occur in the metabolism of organisms before its significance in photosynthesis was appreciated. In nonphotosynthetic organisms of all kinds, the oxidation of phosphoglyceraldehyde to phosphoglyceric acid (the reverse of the course of events in photosynthesis) provides the organism with some energy for metabolism. During the biological *oxidation* of one molecule of phosphoglyceraldehyde to phosphoglyceric acid, one new high-energy phosphate bond is produced. This phosphate group is conserved, together with the energy in the bond, and transferred to adenosinediphosphate (ADP) to make adenosinetriphosphate (ATP). The latter compound is the principal, readily convertible, metabolic currency of the cell; the energy temporarily stored in some of its phosphate bonds can be used directly in any one of a large number of biological reactions. Also, in the course of this oxidation, two hydrogen atoms from phosphoglyceraldehyde are used to reduce a pyridine nucleotide ($PN + 2[H] \longrightarrow PNH_2$).

These observations on phosphoglyceraldehyde metabolism led to the suggestion that in photosynthesis the reverse of this process might occur; that is, that the *reduction* of phosphoglyceric acid to phosphoglyceraldehyde might be driven by reduced pyridine nucleotides and ATP produced at the expense of light in the chloroplast.

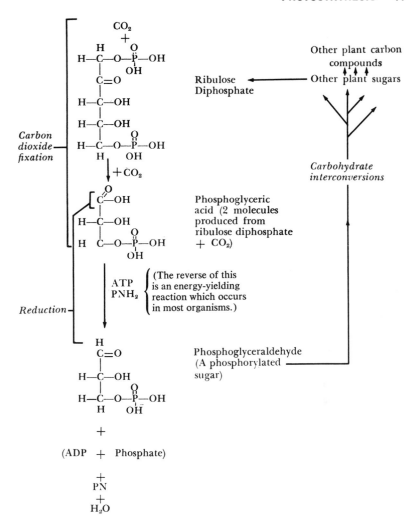

FIG. 3–10. The path of carbon: From CO_2 to phosphoglyceraldehyde, the first sugar in the path, and through a large number of enzymatic steps to produce the other sugars of the plant. One of the sugars is ribulose diphosphate which combines with CO_2 to form a compound which splits into two molecules of phosphoglyceric acid. This organic acid is reduced to the sugar, phosphoglyceraldehyde. The light energy absorbed for photosynthesis is fed into the carbon path in the form of the energy contained in the chemical bond between the second and third phosphate in adenosine triphosphate (ATP). The energy of this bond is consumed in the reduction of phosphoglyceric acid to phosphoglyceraldehyde and thus adenosine diphosphate (ADP) plus free phosphate appear from the ATP. The hydrogen atoms from the water used in photosynthesis are introduced into the path of carbon as PNH_2.

Ultimately, Daniel Arnon and his collaborators at the University of California at Berkeley discovered that suspensions of chloroplasts isolated from spinach leaves can produce ATP from light, ADP, and inorganic phosphorus. At about the same time, Albert Frenkel of the University of Minnesota found that the minute chromatophores of photosynthetic bacteria could also perform "photosynthetic phosphorylation." The addition of inorganic phosphate to ADP (to form ATP) can easily be demonstrated by conducting experiments with radio-phosphorus. The rate of incorporation of phosphate into ATP serves as an assay for determining the activity of the system. Now as we start again toward the phosphoglyceric acid—phosphoglyceraldehyde junction down the path of energy from light, we know that the fountainheads of reduced pyridine nucleotides (PNH_2) and adenosinetriphosphate (ATP) will mark the proper path.

Electrons and energy. Before beginning this part of the excursion, it is worthwhile to consider electrons and energy in a more general way. Electrons are all the same—but not quite. One difference among electrons is the amount of energy they may possess. An electron combined with oxygen in H_2O is completely oxidized and so has no energy available to biological systems. On the other hand, an electron combined with carbon at the level of a carbohydrate has a great deal of energy. This energy can be released in a number of ways and converted into any one of a number of forms.

Let us take two nonbiological examples of energy release. When a piece of wood burns, the electrons fall down through a large energy span; the light we see and the heat we feel are forms of energy generated as the electrons of cellulose combine with oxygen to form water. In electricity, on the other hand, the electrons fall down through a potential span, whether or not they combine with oxygen, and the energy released appears as heat, light, or mechanical work, depending upon the apparatus used.

In our experiment of burning wood, the oxidation occurred rapidly and in a relatively uncontrolled way. In biological systems, oxidations occur in steps and in systems where the fall of an electron through an energy span is coupled with the production of high-energy chemical bonds that can be used in a number of ways. For example, we saw reduced pyridine nucleotides (PNH_2) produced during the *oxidation* of phosphoglyceraldehyde to phosphoglyceric acid. As the two electrons on PNH_2 move toward oxygen to form water, each electron is handed from one acceptor to another, rather than falling through the entire span at once. Each acceptor is at a particular rung on the energy ladder. As the electrons move down from rung to rung, the energy that is yielded is used to make new high-energy phosphate bonds on ATP. We do not know in detail how the fall of an electron through an energy span is coupled with the production of high-energy phosphate bonds. We do know, however, that this process occurs in highly organized intercellular structures, the mitochondria, and that among the acceptors waiting at each energy rung to take an electron and then

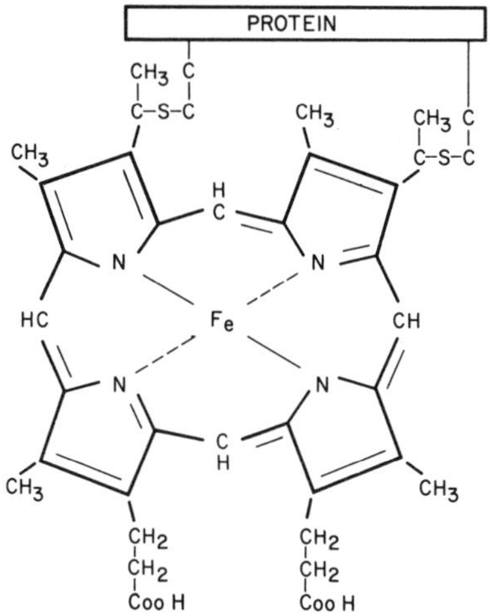

FIG. 3–11. Representation of the structure of a heme molecule of cytochrome *c* showing the way in which the porphyrin ring is attached to the protein. Contrary to the impression given here, the protein portion of cytochrome *c* is more than ten times larger (by weight) than a heme. It is the iron of the heme which can be in either the oxidized $Fe+++$ or reduced $Fe++$ state.

pass it to the acceptor at the next rung are iron-containing porphyrin-protein compounds: the cytochromes (Fig. 3–11). When the iron of a cytochrome is in its $Fe+++$ state, it can accept an electron (it is reduced) and become $Fe++$ (i.e., $Fe+++ + e- \longrightarrow Fe++$); this process is reversible. The cytochromes differ from one another chemically in the nature of the porphyrin and protein of which they are composed; they differ functionally in the potential (energy) span through which they are active.

Since a cytochrome can take up or donate electrons—that is, be reversibly oxidized and reduced (Cytochrome $Fe++ \leftrightarrows$ Cytochrome $Fe+++ + e-$), a specific kind of cytochrome can carry electrons from one energy level to another through its potential span. (Our peculiar ladder seems to have elastic rungs.) This goes on as long as there are electrons available at the high-energy end of this cytochrome's span and as long as there is a supply of electron-acceptor molecules (for example, another $Fe+++$ cytochrome) available at the low-energy end of the span (Fig. 3–12).

A cytochrome in the reduced ($Fe++$) condition absorbs different wavelengths of light than the same cytochrome in the oxidized ($Fe+++$) state; consequently, its color reveals whether it has already taken up an electron or is prepared to donate one. With extremely sensitive special equipment, the oxidation and reduction of cytochromes can be observed in whole cells or suspensions of extracted mitochondria (Fig. 3–13). Changes in the absorption spectra due to shifts of cytochromes between $Fe++$ and $Fe+++$ conditions

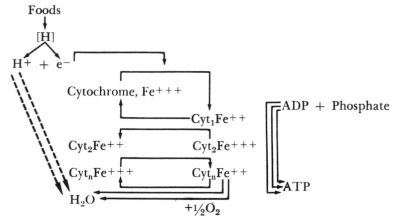

FIG. 3-12. As an electron drops through an energy span in a biological system, it is handed from one acceptor to another. Here, the iron of each cytochrome (all have fictitious names in this sketch; real cytochromes include cytochrome a, b, c, etc.) is shown to be reduced ($e^- + Fe^{+++} \longrightarrow Fe^{++}$) as it accepts an electron and then oxidized ($Fe^{++} \longrightarrow Fe^{+++} + e^-$) as it gives this electron to the next cytochrome. Each cytochrome operates through a fixed potential (energy) range. The fall of an electron through the potential span is coupled, in some as yet undefined way, to the formation of high energy phosphate bonds—that is, adenosinetriphosphate is made from adenosine diphosphate and phosphate.

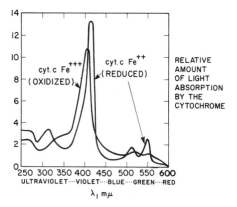

FIG. 3-13. Absorption spectra of oxidized (Fe^{+++}) and reduced (Fe^{++}) cytochrome c. Note the absorption of 550 millimicrons (green) light by the reduced cytochrome compared to the oxidized form. With preparations of mitochondria from living cells, and in some cases in intact cells, changes in absorption maxima can be observed as oxygen is admitted or removed. [From E. Margoliash, *British Medical Bulletin*, Vol. 9 (1953), p. 89. Reproduced by permission of the Medical Department of The British Council.]

follow the exhaustion or introduction of oxygen or food; this provides direct evidence that cytochromes participate in electron transport in biological systems. In photosynthesis, light energy is used to raise electrons from a low energy level—that is, from their combination with oxygen in water—to an energy level high enough to permit them to add to carbon and contribute to the formation of carbohydrates. Electrons are pushed, or pulled, up an energy ladder in photosynthesis; the rungs of this ladder are not identical with those an electron descends during biological oxidation or respiration, although there are marked similarities.

Early photosynthetic events. With this background, we can now try to discuss the beginning of the process of photosynthesis. The primary event in photosynthesis is the absorption of a quantum of light by a photosynthetically active pigment such as chlorophyll *a*. It will be remembered that the reduction of a molecule of phosphoglyceric acid to the sugar phosphoglyceraldehyde requires a molecule of reduced pyridine nucleotide (PNH_2) plus a molecule of ATP. How is the energy of an absorbed quantum used to raise an electron in water to an energy level high enough to enable it to reduce PN (that is, $2e^- + 2H^+$ ———→ PNH_2)? How is the energy of a quantum converted, in whole or part, to chemical bond energy in ATP? Although these questions cannot be answered completely, it seems worthwhile to explore the areas in which the solutions seem to lie.

First, what happens when a chlorophyll molecule absorbs a quantum of light, or perhaps better, *why* does the chlorophyll molecule absorb a quantum of energy? We have already seen from their absorption spectra (Fig. 3–2) that chlorophylls preferentially absorb photons of blue and red light. Why these photons? Photons differ from one another in the amount of energy they contain; thus, a photon of blue light contains considerably more energy than a photon of red light. Furthermore, the energy of the photon is given up entirely or not at all; either a whole photon is converted into another form of energy or the quantum remains unchanged. On the other hand, the absorption spectrum of a molecule is a function of the arrangement of its component atoms and particularly of the electron fields surrounding these atoms. Electrons are usually paired in specific orbitals; each orbital is a different energy level. Only those photons are absorbed that have sufficient energy to move one of the electrons to a new and higher *available* orbital or completely out of the field of the molecule. The latter phenomenon is *photo-ionization*, the production of a pair of ions—a positively charged pigment plus a negatively charged electron—at the expense of light energy. Thus absorption of a photon really means that its energy has been converted into the energy of an electron.

This process is analogous to the now familiar process of putting a satellite into orbit. The fuel, solid or liquid, is used to take the large rocket out of its "ground state" at the surface of the earth and place it into a higher energy state in orbit around the earth; or, if enough energy is supplied, the rocket can be pushed entirely out of the gravitational field of the earth. Just like the rocket, the activated electron tends to fall back to its original ground state;

and, in so doing, it releases the energy of the photon that pushed it out of its ground state. This energy can appear in a number of ways. It can appear as heat, just as when a rocket falls back through the earth's atmosphere. It can be converted into photons of longer wavelength (that is, lower energy) than the photon that was absorbed by the pigment; we see this form of energy as fluorescent or luminescent light (the difference between fluorescence and luminescence is the time during which the photon is emitted). Or the energy released during the return to the ground state can drive a system performing "useful" work.

In photosynthesis, a photon is absorbed by a photosynthetic pigment, and an electron of this pigment is raised to a higher energy level; the entire molecule is excited if one of its electrons is raised to a higher energy level. The newly acquired energy of some excited pigment molecules may be released as fluorescence as the pigment returns to its ground state, but the energy of most of the excited pigment molecules is conserved and used to do photosynthetic work. There is still considerable argument as to whether in photosynthesis an electron is moved to a new higher-energy orbital or whether it is expelled completely from the chlorophyll molecule—that is, whether photo-ionization occurs. There is also considerable uncertainty as to exactly how the energy of this electron is harnessed for useful work in photosynthesis. We do know, however, that this energy ultimately appears in a high-energy phosphate linkage in the third phosphate bond of ATP; and also that, somewhere along the line in photosynthesis by higher green plants, oxygen atoms from water are released into the atmosphere, while a pair of electrons, presumably arising ultimately from water, are used to reduce pyridine nucleotides.

A model that is easy to comprehend but may or may not be completely correct has been outlined by Arnon and other workers. Here it is assumed that when a photon is absorbed by chlorophyll the electron that is excited is completely expelled from the field of the chlorophyll molecule (that is, photo-ionization occurs) and is accepted by some other reducible (that is, electron-accepting) component of the photosynthetic apparatus. This assumption has two immediate consequences. First, the chlorophyll molecule that has lost an electron has a great affinity for another one to replace it; and, second, the reduced acceptor now has a new electron at a high energy level. By being handed down through a series of electron carriers, in a manner analogous to that described for oxidative respiration in mitochondria, the energy of this electron could be used to produce high-energy phosphate bonds. The electron itself could ultimately be used to reduce pyridine nucleotides. The chlorophyll molecule, which would still have an electron gap, could acquire a replacement electron directly or indirectly from water. The oxygen atoms of water would then be released as O_2 (Fig. 3–14).

Another suggestion, with the same end result, is that the energy of the photon that is absorbed by chlorophyll is used directly to remove an electron from

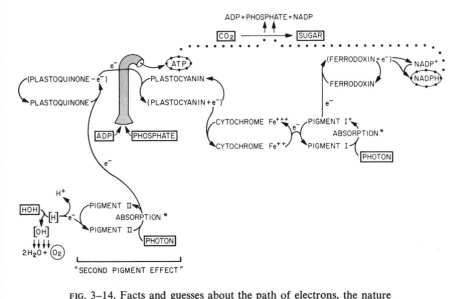

FIG. 3–14. Facts and guesses about the path of electrons, the nature of the action of light, and of the site and mechanism of photophosphorylation in photosynthesis. These facts are: light is absorbed, oxygen is released, ATP is formed from ADP and inorganic phosphate, and pyridine nucleotide (NADP) is reduced. (The reduced pyridine nucleotide and the ATP are used then to reduce carbon from CO_2 to carbon in a sugar.) The second photoreaction, thought to be mediated by light absorbed by "accessory pigments," may lie somewhere around the region marked "Second Pigment Effect."
* "Absorption" means that the light energy (that is, the energy of the photon) might have been absorbed by one of the light-gathering pigment molecules and then transferred, not as light, to the pigment at the "Active Center." Such events might occur to activate Pigment I (which could be P-700) and Pigment II (which could be another special form of chlorophyll *a*) or both Pigment I and Pigment II.

water. According to this view, the splitting of water, which requires a good deal of energy, is somehow coupled with the energy-yielding return of an excited chlorophyll molecule to its ground state. Regardless of whether this so-called "water splitting" occurs as an early or late step in the path of energy, the hypotheses are all adjusted to account for the fact that oxygen is released in photosynthesis by higher green plants.

The phenomenon of the formation of high-energy phosphate bonds at the expense of energy from photons is known as *photophosphorylation*. The scheme already described, which represents one of two kinds of photophosphorylation that have been observed, is called *noncyclic* photophosphorylation. The other kind of photophosphorylation is called *cyclic* photophosphorylation.

In noncyclic photophosphorylation, as we have seen, a quantum of light is absorbed, oxygen is evolved, new high-energy phosphate bonds are formed, and pyridine nucleotides are reduced. In cyclic photophosphorylation, high-energy phosphate bonds are formed following the absorption of light quanta, but oxygen is not evolved and pyridine nucleotides are not reduced; that is, even though an electron may be going through a series of electron carriers and its energy converted to that of high-energy phosphate bonds, the electron itself is never delivered as part of the reduced pyridine nucleotide. One of the mechanisms suggested to explain cyclic photophosphorylation assumes the ejection of an electron from chlorophyll excited by light, analogous to the one scheme we have already discussed, and the passage of this electron through the same kind of chain as in noncyclic photophosphorylation. However, this electron returns to the chlorophyll molecule, which has a high affinity for an electron because of its loss of this same electron. In the course of the high-energy electron's falling back to the ground state through the electron-transport system, high-energy phosphate bonds are made. Another possibility is that the oxygen that would be liberated if the chlorophyll acquired an electron from water might recombine with the electron that has passed through the transport system. The net result here too would be the failure of oxygen to be released and the failure of pyridine nucleotides to be reduced.

How to follow electrons.   The problem of understanding the path of carbon in photosynthesis was elegantly solved by following the carbon-14 from $C^{14}O_2$. The connecting thread in the path of energy is the electron. Can it be followed? As we have seen, electrons differ from one another by their energy; they may also differ in the direction of their spin. Both of these properties are currently being exploited to try to trace the path of these minute, negatively charged particles in photosynthesis.

We can follow electrons during their descent through an energy stepladder by looking at color changes in the rungs; many of these rungs are iron porphyrin proteins (that is, cytochromes). As we have already discussed, each iron atom in a cytochrome can be either in the oxidized, ferric ($Fe+++$), state; or it can accept an electron and thus be reduced to the ferrous ($Fe++$) state. A reduced (ferrous) cytochrome has a different light-absorption pattern (absorption spectrum) from an oxidized (ferric) one; consequently, the ferric and ferrous states can be distinguished in a spectrophotometer, and the addition or removal of an electron can thus be detected. Britton Chance of the University of Pennsylvania has devised a very sensitive, extremely rapid spectrophotometer, which is capable of detecting changes in the absorption spectra of cytochromes in suspensions of intact organisms. Certain cytochromes change from the $Fe++$ to the $Fe+++$ condition when photosynthetic bacteria are illuminated. This observation shows that these cytochromes are almost certainly involved in photosynthetic electron transport.

Barry Commoner at Washington University in St. Louis, Melvin Calvin and Daniel Arnon, and others have used the spinning characteristics of electrons to study their path in photosynthesis. Each electron carries a unit negative charge, which acts like a small magnet. In compounds having an even number of electrons, the magnetic field of one spinning electron normally is exactly canceled by that of another electron spinning in the opposite direction in the same orbital. A compound in which all of the electrons are paired is *diamagnetic*. Such a compound has no intrinsic magnetic properties and aligns itself in a magnetic field at right angles to the field. A molecule containing an unpaired electron is termed *paramagnetic;* it aligns itself by its north and south poles within the magnetic field in which it is placed. The magnetic properties of a paramagnetic substance can be detected, and its magnetic moment can be measured. Obviously, free unpaired electrons not part of a molecule can also be detected.

The most sensitive device for detecting free electrons or *free radicals,* as organic molecules with unpaired electrons are called, is the electron spin, or electron paramagnetic, resonance spectrophotometer. Some instruments of this kind can measure as few as 10^{11} molecules of a free radical or the same number of free electrons. The interesting observation has been made that unpaired electrons appear when photosynthetic cells are illuminated. A few different kinds of signals have been observed, suggesting the development of two different species of such materials. The exact significance of these findings has been argued; probably only after considerably more work has been done will their meaning be clearly understood. However, this observation is one of the first indications that it will be possible to detect early light-driven changes in electron states. These events all occur prior to the production of reduced pyridine nucleotides in noncylic photophosphorylation.

An Enhanced View of Photosynthesis and the Photosynthetic Apparatus

So far we have considered an almost completely "stripped-down" version of photosynthesis—no accessories, no frills. At this level photosynthesis is *comparatively* uncomplicated, though obviously many parts are poorly understood. The hypotheses described were selected because they are relatively easy to understand and may also bear a close relationship to the truth. However, in order to appreciate more fully the status of present research in this field, we must consider some features of "deluxe"—real life—photosynthesis. This examination will lead us back to the problem of chloroplast ultrastructure—this time at a level below the resolving power of the electron microscope.

The photosynthetic unit. In the discussion up to this point, each chlorophyll molecule has been visualized as acting independently of all others as a light absorber, etc. This is not true; functionally, chlorophyll molecules act in groups. How can this be demonstrated? Suppose each chlorophyll molecule did act independently. Then the photosynthetic apparatus of the cell would be saturated with light only when the number of photons absorbed equaled the number of chlorophyll molecules present. In practice, a number of different, carefully measured doses of light quanta are injected as very short flashes of light into a group of cells. The smallest number of quanta per flash required for saturation of the system is determined (by measuring oxygen release). This number of photons is then compared with the number of chlorophyll molecules in the cells that were exposed. (The chlorophyll is assayed by extracting the pigment from the cells and then measuring its concentration in the extract with a spectrophotometer.) Studies of this kind have indicated that the photosynthetic apparatus is saturated when *about* one chlorophyll molecule in four hundred is absorbing light. Thus, chlorophyll molecules act in groups of about four hundred; * these groups are called *photosynthetic units*. When one pigment molecule in such a group has absorbed a quantum of light, no other chlorophyll molecule in the unit can do so until the excitation energy is discharged as emitted fluorescence or in doing photosynthetic work. The excitation energy appears to be moving about in the unit so rapidly that when a photon hits any chlorophyll molecule within an already excited photosynthetic unit the second quantum is not absorbed. An important point here is that the *energy* of the photon absorbed by one chloro-phyll molecule in the unit can be transferred to another pigment molecule within the same unit.

Engelmann and several subsequent research workers observed that the action spectrum for photosynthesis by red and blue-green algae has a maximum in the orange-green region of the spectrum. This spectral region lies between the two major absorption peaks of chlorophyll—one in red light, another in blue light. This observation indicates that photons absorbed by the phycobilins, the bile pigment-protein complexes present in these algae that absorb light in the orange-green region of the spectrum, can be used for photosynthesis. From the time of Engelmann, biologists have observed that blue-green and red algae have evolved a mechanism for using green light for photosynthesis, since many of these species live in regions of the sea where blue and red light do not filter down to them.

By other techniques it has been shown that (light) energy absorbed by the phycobilins, phycocyanin and phycoerythin, is transferred to the chlorophyll *a,* which is also present in these organisms. Duysens in Holland illuminated algal cells with a color of light which is absorbed almost entirely by the bile pigment-protein complex but hardly at all by chlorophyll *a*. He then measured the fluores-cence of the chlorophyll *a*. (Fluorescence-emission spectra of pigments are as characteristic as their light-absorption spectra.) In these experiments, although the phycobilins absorbed almost all the light taken up by the cells, the chloro-phyll *a* emitted as much light as when chlorophyll *a* itself was the absorbing pigment. The experiments, then, showed that the energy absorbed as light by the phycobilins is transferred to chlorophyll *a*. As pointed out in a previous

---

* "About four hundred" is *liberally* translated from a number of experiments, some of which indicate that as many as 2,600 chlorophyll molecules may be functionally interrelated.

part of this discussion, excited molecules can dissipate energy and return to their ground state by emitting light as fluorescence. Duysens assumed that a fixed percentage of the excited molecules, or photosynthetic units, lose their excitation energy by fluorescing; the remainder use the energy to do photosynthetic work. Thus, the intensity of the fluorescence of chlorophyll *a* in a sample of algal cells is a measure of the total number of chlorophyll *a* molecules excited (regardless of whether excitation is direct) by absorption of photons, or by acceptance of energy absorbed initially as light by phycobilins. In a series of similar experiments with brown and green algae, it was found that regardless of whether carotenoids (the yellow and orange chloroplast pigments) or other chlorophylls (for example, chlorophyll *b* in green algae) absorb most of the light, it is always the chlorophyll *a* that fluoresces. From this finding, two conclusions were drawn. (1) The chloroplast pigments other than chlorophyll *a* act as accessory light absorbers. They absorb light energy and become excited. The energy is transferred to chlorophyll *a*, which is the only pigment that plays a role beyond light absorption in photosynthesis. The energy-transfer mechanism is similar to that by which one chlorophyll *a* molecule transfers energy to another in the same photosynthetic unit. (2) Chlorophyll molecules cannot be seen with the electron microscope, nor can one kind of pigment be distinguished from another; but since one kind of pigment can transfer energy to another, it follows that the accessory pigment molecules must lie very close to the chlorophyll *a* molecules in the organism. Perhaps each photosynthetic unit in, for example, a green alga contains molecules of carotenoids and chlorophyll *b* as well as those of chlorophyll *a*.

Enhancement.   This last hypothesis seemed to provide a perfectly satisfactory explanation of the function and mechanism of action for all of the accessory pigments. However, the entire question of the role of the accessory pigments was thrown open a few years ago by a startling discovery made in Robert Emerson's laboratory at the University of Illinois. When light of two different wavelengths— for example, one absorbed primarily by chlorophyll *a;* the other, primarily by chlorophyll *b*—was shone on green algal cells simultaneously, more photosynthesis was done, that is, more oxygen was released, than when an equal number of quanta were absorbed by chlorophyll *a* alone. This was not to be expected if chlorophyll *b* acted simply as an accessory light absorber. Similar results have been obtained in investigations with other "accessory pigments," and a whole new field of research involving the action spectra of *photosynthetic enhancement* has developed. Jack Myers of the University of Texas has found that Emerson's effect can be seen even if the "enhancing" light and the light that excites chlorophyll *a* are administered a few seconds apart.

There is wide and intense interest in this possible window for looking inside photosynthesis. It now seems possible that the accessory pigments may act directly in the oxygen-release mechanism of photosynthesis, which would place these pigments functionally in the region marked "Possible site of 'second' pigment effect" in Fig. 3–14. If we assume that the absorption of a quantum of light energy by an accessory pigment molecule results in its ionization with the same consequences as outlined for chlorophyll, we then see the part of photosynthesis shown in Fig. 3–14 as a sort of two-stage, light-driven electron-pumping system. As visualized here, an (incomplete) energy drop between the stages may be coupled with the generation of high-energy phosphate bonds—that is, the production of ATP from ADP and phosphate.

These new data do not force us to abandon the notion of light absorption and energy transfer to chlorophyll *a* as one kind of role for other photosynthetically active pigments. However, these data do force us to look upon even the light-absorbing process as being made up of several separate but interdependent phenomena, just as Van Niel's assessment of photosynthesis encouraged the study of $6CO_2 + 6H_2O \longrightarrow C_6H_{12}O_6 + 6O_2$ in rational segments. Furthermore, Emerson's enhancement effects emphasize the possible importance of the incorporation of the other pigments we have been discussing in the same functional unit with chlorophyll *a*.

One more item must be added about chlorophylls in and out of plants. The chlorophylls of a plant can be extracted with acetone or methyl alcohol and then separated from one another. Separation of chloroplast pigments on columns of powdered sugar was pioneered by Tswett in the last century. Two chemically distinct chlorophylls, *a* and *b,* are found together in extracts of higher land plants and green algae. Chlorophylls *c, d,* and *e* have been isolated from various other algae. Each of these pigments is a distinct compound; each has a characteristic absorption spectrum. But inside the living cell the situation is far different. Using special spectrophotometric apparatus, C. S. French and his collaborators at the Carnegie Institute Laboratories at Stanford, California, have discovered that each photosynthetic cell contains not one but at least three kinds of chlorophyll *a*. They can be distinguished from one another within the living cell by the kinds of light each absorbs preferentially; however, extracts of cells with three kinds of chlorophyll *a* contain only one chemical species of the pigment. What does this mean? Possibly that the chemical compound "chlorophyll *a*" is bound into the photosynthetic apparatus in one of several ways and that, perhaps, each form has a separate function.

For a long time, students of photosynthesis have visualized the existence of an "energy sink" within each photosynthetic unit. According to this concept, only one or a few molecules of chlorophyll *a* in each unit is connected to the equipment for doing photosynthesis beyond the act of light absorption. Thus, an entire photosynthetic unit would normally be drained of its excitation energy only when the pigment molecule at the "active center" becomes excited. Could some or one of French's *in vivo* forms of chlorophyll *a* be at the sink? A form of chlorophyll which absorbs far into the red, at about 7000 Å (that is, 700 millimicrons), has been detected and partially separated from other chlorophylls by Bessel Kok. Many investigators believe that this pigment (frequently designated as P-700 because of its absorption at about 700 millimicrons) is at the active center.

Inside the photosynthetic unit. If there is an "active center" within each photosynthetic unit, what might its composition be? According to present ideas it ought to include at least some electron-transport compounds. It is obvious why students of photosynthesis are interested when a new compound is found to be localized in the chloroplast and why they become excited when there is one molecule of the substance for about 400 molecules of chlorophyll.

What are chloroplasts made of besides chlorophylls and carotenoids? One expects, and finds, the enzymes of the carbon path; these account for a great deal of the chloroplast protein. Some other proteins—for example, the proteins to which chlorophylls are absorbed or attached—are not soluble, and their activity (if any) in photosynthesis cannot be studied in solution. Fatty materials, lipids, are found in the chloroplast in moderately high concentration. The alternating layers of electron dense and light areas, seen when thin sections of chloroplasts are examined with the electron microscope, are thought to be regions of high concentration of proteins and fats.

Components of the fat-soluble lamellae—for example, the yellow carotenoids—probably lie in the lipid zones. The lipid-soluble, carotenoid-like, long phytol "tail" of the chlorophyll molecule is probably also buried in the fat layer. On the other hand, the flat porphyrin "head" of the chlorophyll molecule is not so fat-soluble; it may lie just at the interface between a layer of fat and of protein.

Quinones share with cytochromes and pyridine nucleotides the capacity for reversibly accepting and releasing electrons; they can undergo reversible reduction and oxidation. The discovery that certain quinones are localized in the photosynthetic apparatus and participate in the Hill reaction (the photolysis of water, release of oxygen, and reduction of an electron acceptor) suggests that they may play an important role in some early steps in photosynthetically initiated electron transport. Most quinones are water-soluble; but plastoquinone, a quinone with a long, fat-soluble phytol "tail" fundamentally similar to the "tail" on chlorophyll, is present in high concentration in chloroplasts. Is one molecule (or more) of plastoquinone at each "active center"? Do the fat-soluble and water-soluble parts of the plastoquinone molecule help orient it properly in the photosynthetic unit?

On the basis of knowledge about the transfer of electrons through an energy span in mitochondria, we expect to find oxidizable-reducible cytochromes among the components of the "active center" or "energy sink" of each photosynthetic unit. Robin Hill's discovery of two new cytochromes that are found only in photosynthetic cells was welcome and exciting news. This excitement was bolstered when Leo Vernon and Martin Kamen isolated unique cytochromes from photosynthetic bacteria. Some of these cytochromes are very similar to the photosynthetic cytochromes of higher plants in functionally important respects.

Other compounds that can accept or give up electrons have also been identified in chloroplasts and assigned places in the electron transport chain of photosynthesis. These include: Ferredoxin, an iron-protein complex believed to carry electrons between pigment 700 and an enzyme that catalyzes the reduction of pyridine nucleotide; plastocyanin, a copper-protein complex that may carry electrons some place between plastoquinone and the cytochrome that provides electrons to pigment 700; and some pteridines (butterfly wing pigments are also pteridines) that may play a role in the formation of high-energy phosphate bonds in photosynthesis. The position of each electron carrier in the electron transport chain of photosynthesis is judged by the potential range in which the carrier can operate as well as from experiments in which parts of photosynthetic electron transport can be studied in an isolated manner. Figure 3–14 summarizes some current ideas on the electron transport chain of photosynthesis.

One possible scheme for the organization of part of a photosynthetic unit and its active center is shown in Fig. 3–15. The function of the photoreceptor

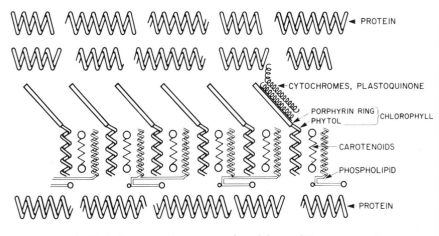

FIG. 3–15. A diagrammatic representation of the possible arrangement of chloroplast components including the hypothetical active center. [From M. Calvin, "The Photochemical Apparatus," *Brookhaven Symposium in Biology*, No. 11 (1958), p. 177. Reproduced by permission.]

is to convert light energy into the energy of a molecule or electron. At the active center, the extra energy of the "excited" molecule or electron is converted into chemical bond energy in ATP, and the partially enervated electron reduces pyridine nucleotide. The ATP and PNH_2, either at the active center or somewhere else in the chloroplast, are consumed in producing sugar.

Problems—Present, Future, and Unseen

One of the nagging problems in photosynthesis has been to try to understand how the energy from several quanta could be pooled to perform what seemed to be a single step. Four is theoretically the minimum of red-light quanta that would have enough energy to remove a pair of electrons from water. Thus the energy from at least two quanta must be pooled to remove a single [H] or electron. (The problem is complicated by experimental values of approximately eight to ten quanta per pair of electrons. We will disregard this question, which relates to the efficiency of the system.) It seems probable that exploration of the extra-accessory role of the so-called (unfortunately) "accessory pigments" will reveal the answer. Current evidence suggests that the energy of one quantum of light absorbed by an accessory pigment may be used in concert with the energy of a quantum absorbed by chlorophyll a.

On the whole, while there are some unresolved points about the path of carbon, the greatest uncertainty surrounds the part of photosynthesis we have called the "path of electrons" starting from the initial act of absorbing a quantum of light. Because of the magnitude of the uncertainty and the very vigorous research interest in it, this is the segment of photosynthesis in which the most significant new discoveries are to be made.

"Applied" photosynthesis is on the verge of a renaissance. The investigation of closed ecological systems, as in space ships, is capturing the imagination and time of many investigators. New ways of growing microscopic and macroscopic plants to provide food and oxygen as well as to convert biological wastes into useful materials are being sought.

We know relatively little about photosynthesis of plants under natural conditions in the field and the seas. New apparatus is being designed and used to gather information on the relationships between environmental conditions, such as temperature, light, and carbon dioxide concentration, and photosynthesis. Our increased knowledge of biochemical mechanisms, both in photosynthesis and other aspects of metabolism, may make it easier to interpret the data from field studies. This understanding is certain to be exploited in meeting the problem of feeding the growing population on earth.

One hundred years from now, the equation $6CO_2 + 6H_2O \longrightarrow C_6H_{12}O_6 + 6O_2$ will probably still be in textbooks, but it will be possible to report on what goes on "inside photosynthesis" with more facts and fewer speculations. If the acquisition of knowledge in this area continues to accelerate at the rate it has during the past thirty years—and this is to be expected—many of the problems we have examined will be replaced by understanding, and the new understanding will bring new problems.

REFERENCES

ALLEN, M. B. *Comparative Biochemistry of Photoreactive Systems*. New York: Academic Press, Inc., 1960.

BONNER, J., AND J. E. VARNER. *Plant Biochemistry*. New York: Academic Press, Inc., 1965.

CLAYTON, R. K. *Molecular Physics in Photosynthesis*. New York: Blaisdell Publishing Co., 1965.

GAFFRON, H. "Photosynthesis." *Plant Physiology,* ed. F. C. Steward. Vol. 1 B, p. 277. New York: Academic Press, Inc., 1960.

HILL, R., AND C. P. WHITTINGHAM. *Photosynthesis.* London: Methuen & Co., Ltd., 1955.

KAMEN, M. D. *Primary Processes in Photosynthesis.* New York: Academic Press, Inc., 1963.

THE MEASUREMENT OF TIME IN PLANTS

4

Beatrice M. Sweeney

Department of Botany
Yale University

The typical plants of the world display a precise and beautiful orientation in space, elongating upward and downward from buried seeds and spreading their leaves at right angles to the incident light from which they derive energy to live and grow. This spatial arrangement has been shown to result from the response of plant cells to the directional factors of the environment, light, and gravity. Plants also show a very orderly behavior with respect to time, not only in the sequence of changes that we think of as growth and differentiation, but in seed germination, flowering, and dormancy.

For many years it was assumed that these apparently time-correlated phenomena were also direct responses to the daily and yearly changes in the environment. There seemed no need to postulate that plants had any means of time measurement other than the crude measurement afforded by the progressive piling up of substances and tissues. However, in recent years botanists have become aware that this kind of explanation alone is not enough to account for all the phenomena in which the measurement of time is manifest. The study of plants that form flowers only at seasons when the days are long or short has shown that both long-day and short-day plants are able to measure the length of the night with amazing accuracy, and that the temperature of the environment, which would be expected to alter drastically the rate of accumulation of substances and the rate of formation of new tissues, does not upset this time measurement. In other words, plants which require a night of a certain minimum duration cannot be "fooled" into flowering with shorter nights by increasing the temperature.

Some understanding about this ability of plants to measure the passing of time in terms of twenty-four-hour intervals is now coming from the study of the widespread diurnal or circadian rhythms in plants and animals. It is these rhythms and what we have been able so far to learn from them about time measurement in plants that will be discussed.

During the 1700s and 1800s, plant physiologists such as Zinn (1759), Sachs (1857), and Pfeffer (1875) noticed that the orientation of plants in space is not always fixed but may change with time of day in a regular and predictable way. For example, while the leaves of the common bean plant *Phaseolus* are spread at right angles to the light during the day, at night they fold together like the segments of a closed fan. These changes, which have been picturesquely called "sleep movements," may be thought of as conferring on the plant the advantage of protecting its leaves from water loss through transpiration at night, when spreading of the leaves is not essential for photosynthetic light absorption and gas exchange. Sleep movements occur in a number of different plants, including many legumes and *Oxalis*.

Figure 4–1 shows the arrangement of the leaflets of *Oxalis* during the day

FIG. 4–1. Sleep movements in *Oxalis*. The position of the leaflets during the day is shown at the left; that during the night, at the right.

and at night. The remarkable thing about these leaf movements is that the position the leaves assume is not a direct result of the light falling on them. This was clearly shown by the investigations of Pfeffer and Sachs, who were curious to know whether folding of the leaves would take place whenever the leaves were darkened. They found that this was not the case, for when plants of the bean were placed in darkness during the day the leaves still folded only at night. In continuous darkness, alternate folding and expanding could be observed several times, and the time between successive foldings was still about twenty-four hours, as it is in plants which are growing in natural light (Fig. 4–2).

Soon botanists began to notice other plant changes that are correlated with time of day. The opening and closing of flowers very commonly show this kind

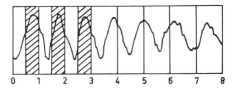

FIG. 4–2. Sleep movements of *Phaseolus* represented graphically. This record, made by a lever attached to a leaf, shows the movement of the leaf during three days and nights, and the continuation of rhythm in the movements when the plant was then placed in continuous light. [From E. Bünning, "Mechanismus and Leistungen der physiologischen Uhr," *Nova Acta Leopoldina N. F.*, Vol. 21 (1959), p. 181. Reproduced by permission.]

of behavior. The Day Lily and the Night-Blooming *Cereus,* flamboyant flowers that they are, come to mind at once, but they are by no means isolated examples of this phenomenon. Recently German researchers have studied this petal movement, using the small flowers of the succulent plant *Kalanchoë* (Fig. 4–3). Secretion of perfume and nectar varies with time of day in some flowers, dramatically

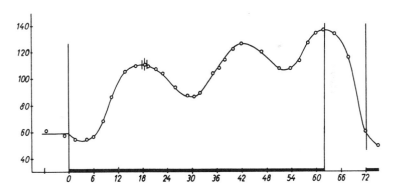

FIG. 4–3. The rhythm in the opening and closing of the petals of *Kalanchoë blossfeldiana.* The abscissa represents the time in hours after the plant was placed in darkness, and the ordinate is the apparent width of the flowers when seen from above in relative units. [From W. Engelmann, "Endogene Rhythmik and photoperiodische Buhirduktion bei *Kalanchoë,*" *Planta,* Vol. 55 (1960), p. 504. Reproduced by permission.]

so in the Night-Blooming Jasmine, as anyone who has had a plant of this fragrant species near his window will testify.

As the study of plant physiology gained momentum, examples of changes in the rate of a number of processes at different times of the day were noted. These changes were at first sources of annoyance to physiologists, who had taken pains to place their plant material under what they considered constant conditions and thus expected constant results. Growth rates of *Avena* coleoptiles, carefully grown in constant temperature rooms under constant darkness, were found to vary in this way. The exudation of sap from cut stumps of the sunflower, *Helianthus,* showed the same pattern. Plants growing in the greenhouse showed a very pronounced difference in the amount of exudate collected at different times of day, the maximum being at noon. When these plants were grown in a darkroom, a cycle in the amount of exudation produced by the plants was still observed; a maximum still occurred every twenty-four hours, even though the light, the temperature, and the nutrient solution in which the plants were growing were kept constant (Fig. 4–4). The plant growth hormone auxin, by the way, only served to accentuate the rhythm.

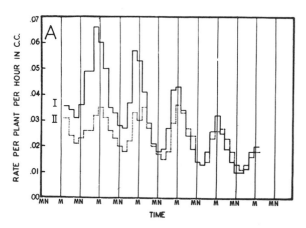

FIG. 4–4. The rhythm in the rate of exudation from cut stumps of *Helianthus* stems in constant darkness and constant temperature. I. With auxin added. II. Without auxin added. [From F. Skoog, T. C. Broyer, and K. A. Grossenbacher, "Effects of Auxin on Rates, Periodicity, and Osmotic Relations in Exudation," *American Journal of Botany,* Vol. 25 (1938), p. 752. Reproduced by permission.]

A number of other physiological processes, including photosynthesis and CO_2 output (Fig. 4–5), have also shown diurnal cycles in constant conditions. It has been known for a long time that cell divisions occur in maximum numbers at certain times of day in organisms in their natural environment. In many cases a diurnal rhythm is operating. In 1921 a study of *Pisum sedativum,* growing in constant conditions, revealed a maximum occurrence of cell division between 9 and 11 in the morning and a minimum between 9 and 11 at night. The same phenomenon has been observed in the filamentous green alga *Spirogyra.* Cell division follows a diurnal rhythm in *Gonyaulax* and a number of other dinoflagellates. The volume of the nucleus (for example, in the common onion) may show diurnal changes.

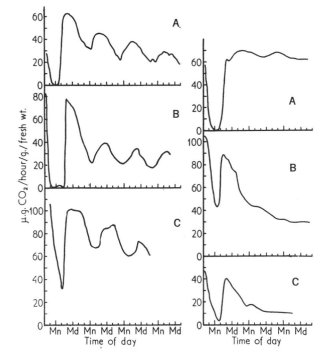

FIG. 4–5. The evolution of carbon dioxide by the leaves of succulents in an atmosphere originally without carbon dioxide during four days in continuous darkness at 26°C. The curves on the left are (A) *Bryophyllum fedtschenkoi;* (B) *B. daigremontianum;* and (C) *B. calycinum.* The curves on the right are (A) *Bryophyllum tubiflorum;* (B) *B. crenatum;* and (C) *Sedum stahlli.* [From M. B. Wilkins, "An Endogenous Rhythm in the Rate of CO_2 Output of Bryophyllum: I, Some Preliminary Experiments," *Journal of Experimental Botany,* Vol. 10 (1959), p. 381. Reproduced by permission.]

Studies of the measurement of the length of the night in photoperiodic plants showed that the sensitivity to light interruptions varies with time and follows a rhythmic pattern, with maxima at intervals of about twenty-four hours. Thus a diurnal rhythm probably underlies this example of time measurement in plants. Diurnal rhythms are observed in animals also, and provide the basis for diurnal and nocturnal behavior in such creatures as nocturnal rodents, bats, and the diurnal chaffinches.

The highly organized multicellular plants and animals are not alone in their manifestation of diurnal rhythmicity. The type of growth of mold mycelium and the discharge of spores of mold and an alga show a diurnal pattern. Unicellular organisms also often possess diurnal rhythms, some of which have now been very carefully investigated. For example, in *Euglena,* the green flagellate, the ability to respond phototactically to light is not constant with time, even in continuous darkness of very long duration. Very pronounced maxima and minima occur within a period of about twenty-four hours irrespective of the temperature, which is also kept constant. The luminescent marine dinoflagellate *Gonyaulax polyedra* shows a pronounced rhythm in its ability to emit light (Fig. 4–6), the

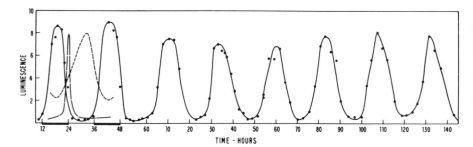

FIG. 4–6. The rhythm in the luminescence in *Gonyaulax polyedra* in alternating light and darkness for two days and from then on in continuous light of low intensity (150 ft. c). One maximum in the rhythms of cell division (broken line with long dashes) and photosynthesis (broken line with short dashes) are shown diagramatically. [From J. W. Hastings, "Biochemical Aspects of Rhythms," Cold Spring Harbor Symposium on Quantitative Biology. *Biological Clocks.* Vol. 25 (1960), p. 134. Reproduced by permission.]

maximum light production coinciding in nature with midnight. This rhythm continues to be present both in constant darkness (for several days) and in continuous light (for at least as long as the patience of the investigator lasted— about two weeks). In *Gonyaulax* it is interesting that photosynthesis and cell division also proceed rhythmically, although the maximum for each is found in a different part of the diurnal cycle—greatest photosynthesis being possible at noon while all cell division takes place during a short time following dawn (Fig. 4–6). These rhythms also persist without environmental changes in light or temperature. Additional examples of diurnal rhythms are found almost daily as more organisms are examined in this regard.

These curious, apparently autonomous changes with time of day, independent of any detectable environmental variable, were at first regarded by biologists with great suspicion. They felt that they were at fault in setting up their "constant" conditions and would soon discover the means of correcting the discrepancy. As time went on and no simple explanation was provided for diurnal changes, which still occurred under constant conditions, biologists began to adopt a new attitude toward diurnal rhythms. In the last ten years, principally through the re-examination of a number of rhythms in both plants and animals by Pittendrigh and Bruce, biologists have increasingly come to think that in diurnal rhythms we see the overt effects of a timekeeping mechanism—"a biological clock." It is increasingly clear that this clock is of great importance in many if not all organisms, and that the ability to keep time may be a property of all living cells.

The question of importance now becomes, "How does this biological clock work? Is it the same in all organisms or are there many kinds of clocks, perhaps many in a single organism which shows a number of diurnal rhythms?" The mechanical clocks which man has devised operate according to several different principles. First, there are hourglass clocks, the most primitive timekeeping mechanical devices, which measure only a single time interval. Once the sand has run through in one direction, the clock stops measuring time until turned by an external agent. Then there are electric clocks, which run continuously but depend on the sixty cycles of alternating current from outside to provide a time signal. Finally, there are the spring- and weight-driven clocks, where the information concerning time is provided by an internal oscillating mechanism. The facts we know about diurnal rhythms make it clear that the biological clock is not of the hourglass type, since many cycles can be observed without time gaps. However, biologists have argued heatedly as to whether or not the biological clock receives rhythmically repeated signals from the environment and thus is in essence similar to the electric clock. The earth is rotating around the sun, and therefore such rhythmic cues are present in the environment and have the same twenty-four-hour period. But since diurnal rhythms continue in constant light and temperature, it is unlikely that these environmental variables act as time cues.

However, there are other factors in the environment that change with time of day and are correlated with the earth's rotation or with man's daily activities, and these variables are not usually controlled in laboratory experiments. One of them is atmospheric pressure. Experiments in which the rate of respiration of potato tubers, measured in a barostat under constant pressure, showed a diurnal rhythm would seem to eliminate pressure as a time cue. However, since the diurnally varying component of atmospheric pressure is quite small compared to the fluctuations from day to day correlated with the weather, this variable would provide an unreliable cue for timekeeping. Variation in cosmic-ray activity or the earth's magnetic field has also been hypothesized, but these variables come up against the same objection as atmospheric pressure, in that random fluctuations are usually much greater than those showing a diurnal pattern.

Since the discovery of the marked effects of smog on plant growth, it has been suggested that diurnal rhythms might represent response to varying smog content of the atmosphere correlated with man's industrial activity or his use of the automobile. Experiments in a smog-free atmosphere, in the Earhart Laboratory at California Institute of Technology, suggest that in some cases—as, for example, the rhythm of growth of the *Avena* coleoptile in darkness—changes in smog content of the air may be responsible.

In most instances, biological timekeeping is probably not linked directly to any environmental factor that varies with the rotation of the earth or man's activities. Under constant conditions many rhythms run with a period which is not *exactly* twenty-four hours but may be slightly longer or shorter, and in a given organism the length of the period is not absolutely fixed but shows a slight temperature and light dependence. Rhythms running in constant conditions, with a period differing no matter how slightly from twenty-four hours, eventually change their phase relationship to the earth's rotation and to day and night. This change is continuous, so that the time at which the maximum of a rhythmic process takes place spans the solar day. We are then faced with the very real probability that the biological clock is of the oscillator type and that these oscillations are autonomous to cells.

If the clock is inside the organism, where is it? Since many unicellular creatures show rhythms, and, in fact, a rhythm in photosynthesis has been demonstrated within a single isolated cell, we cannot invoke intercellular actions. Each cell can contain a whole functional biological clock. But where is it, and of what is it made? The question of the location of the clock within some subcellular component of the cell is still unanswered. There is evidence, however, that it is not housed in the nucleus, since (as has been shown in *Acetabularia*, a unicellular alga that can live normally for months without a nucleus) the rhythm in photosynthesis continues unimpaired and can even be reset after the nucleus has been removed—an easy operation in this plant where the nucleus remains in the rhizoidal part of the plant and cutting causes slight damage (Fig. 4–7).

As is the biologist's habit when considering the function of a single cell, we should now like to refer to biochemistry. What can be said about the biochemistry of timekeeping from a consideration of the biological rhythms? First, it is abundantly clear that the biochemical mechanism for timekeeping cannot be located in the physiological processes that show a diurnal rhythm. Physiological processes like photosynthesis and cell division demonstrate a decided temperature dependence, whereas rhythms show almost none (Fig. 4–8). The observation that inducing luminescence in *Gonyaulax,* and thereby presumably altering the concentration of luciferin, has no effect on the phase or period of the luminescent rhythm supports this view. In *Gonyaulax,* photosynthesis, which is rhythmic, may be entirely inhibited by a specific inhibitor and leave unchanged the rhythm in luminescence. Similarly, cell division may be inhibited completely either by low light intensity or by colchicine or chloramphenicol without eliminating the rhythm in luminescence. It could be argued that the three rhythmic processes in *Gonyaulax* are each controlled by a different clock. However, this seems unlikely, although not impossible, since all three rhythms show the same resetting behavior and the same changes in the period length with temperature.

The attractive hypothesis that relates timekeeping to deoxyribonucleic acid (DNA) function or to the synthesis of ribonucleic acid (RNA) seems to be

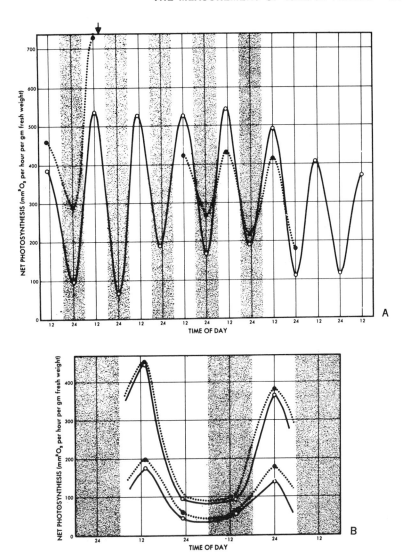

FIG. 4–7. The rhythm in photosynthesis in *Acetabularia* with and without a nucleus. Curve (A) shows the photosynthesis in mature plants with caps (solid line) and in immature plants (dotted line) of *A. major* from which the nucleus was removed at the arrow. The lower curve (B) shows that the rhythm in the rate of photosynthesis in *A. crenulata* may be reset without a nucleus (black dot) as well as when the nucleus is present (white dot). In curve (B) the upper two curves are for mature plants; the lower two, immature. [From Sweeney and F. T. Haxo, "Persistence of a Photosynthetic Rhythm in Enucleated *Acetabularia*," *Science*, Vol. 134 (1961), p. 1362. Reprinted from *Science* by permission.]

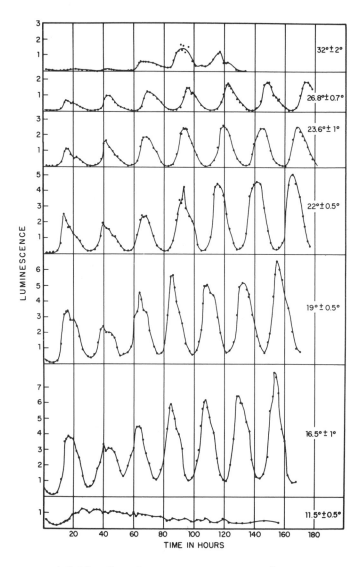

FIG. 4–8. The effect of temperature on the rhythm in luminescence in *Gonyaulax polyedra* in continuous light. Notice that there is only a very small change in the length of the period, or the time between maxima, as the temperature is changed. [From J. W. Hastings and Sweeney, "On the Mechanism of Temperature Independence in a Biological Clock," *Proceedings of the Natural Academy of Science*, Vol. 43 (1957), p. 806. Reproduced by permission.]

rendered less tenable by the observation that rhythmicity can continue without the nucleus, the principal site of DNA activity.

Like all man-made clocks, biological clocks may be reset. This enables the clocks to stay in phase with the day and night and has proven a very convenient property for the biologist studying rhythms in the laboratory, since, in the process he is studying, the time at which maxima occur can be adjusted to suit his convenience. This resetting is most easily accomplished by single light treatments, although temperature pulses are also effective. Resetting was first accomplished by reversing night and day; that is, by darkening the organism during the day and providing artificial light at night for several days. However, this procedure is not necessary; a single light treatment, sometimes of very short duration, is sufficient, provided that the light is given at the proper time. In all plants and animals studied in this way, this "proper time" has turned out to be the middle of the dark period. The sensitivity to reset shows a most interesting diurnal rhythmicity of its own. In *Gonyaulax,* for instance, an investigation of the resetting behavior of the luminescent rhythm showed that no resetting occurs when the light period falls at minimum luminescence. As the light period is given later, more and more reset occurs, until, as the time of maximum luminescence approaches, the reset becomes maximal (Fig. 4–9). After the maximum in luminescence is passed, light produces progressively less reset. Other organisms, notably the single-cell alga *Euglena* and the flying squirrel, show similar changes in sensitivity to reset—an observation which suggests that the mechanism of the biological clock is the same in all cells. The quality of light which brings about resetting differs from organism to organism, however, and so the pigments absorbing the effective light must be different.

Attempts have been made, using *Gonyaulax,* to learn something about the biochemistry of timekeeping by bringing about resetting with chemical treatments of a pulsed nature. While some transitory changes were effected, no chemical among the large collection assayed in this way proved as effective as light.

Since we cannot assume that the biochemistry of the biological clock is in any way intimately connected with that of the rhythmic processes being measured, we must be very careful, in biochemical studies with inhibitors and stimulating substances, not to confuse effects on the observed rhythms from those on the clockwork itself. Substances causing the disappearance of a rhythm do not necessarily affect the clock, but may only inhibit the process being measured. If, however, the period of the rhythm is changed following administration of a substance, this may provide evidence that this material has actually altered the timekeeping mechanism. So far investigations have shown that the clock is resistant to changes mediated by chemicals. This avenue of approach to clock biochemistry has not proved fruitful. Very high concentrations of several inhibitors, including cyanide, have been shown to lengthen the period of the rhythm in *Phaseolus.* In *Gonyaulax* only two of a number of substances assayed have any effect—colchicine, which lengthens the period in the luminescent rhythm; and chloramphenicol, an inhibitor of protein synthesis, which shortens the period. These findings have not thus far led to useful interpretations regarding clock biochemistry, but they are interesting in another respect. The tem-

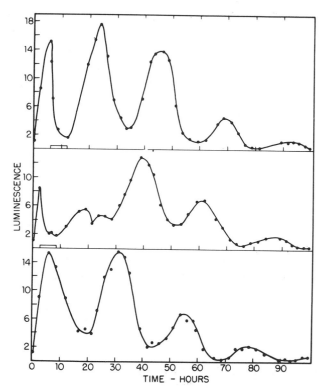

FIG. 4–9. Resetting the rhythm in luminescence in *Gonyaulax polyedra* with a light pulse. The lower curve shows the luminescence of the control, in continuous darkness since zero time on the abscissa. The upper two curves show the response of cells kept under identical conditions with the exception of a 6-hour light exposure (1400 ft. c.) given at the times indicated by the bars on the time axis. [From J. W. Hastings and Sweeney, "The *Gonyaulax* Clock," *Photoperiodism and Related Phenomena in Plants and Animals,* Publication 55 of the AAAS (1959), p. 579. Reproduced by permission.]

perature independence of rhythms is thought to indicate that the clock mechanism comprises at least two reactions, each of which is temperature dependent; but the products of one inhibit the rate of the other in the manner of a feedback control. The findings regarding the effects of chemicals on timekeeping suggest that these two reactions are similar in their sensitivity to inhibitors.

That we should not be completely discouraged from the search for an intracellular biological clock is suggested by experiments with heavy water. These experiments show that in *Euglena* grown in a deuterated medium, the period of the rhythm in phototaxis during continuous darkness is much longer than that in nondeuterated cultures. This implies a physical or biochemical participation of the hydrogen atom in timekeeping.

Another approach to clock biochemistry is the quantitative study of cell components at different times in the cycle under constant conditions. For example, it has been demonstrated that in *Gonyaulax* the enzyme and substrate of the light-producing reaction vary in amount with time of day. It is interesting that, contrary to what might be expected, many substances within the cell do not show diurnal variations, such as the incorporation of radioactive sulfur and phosphorus. Evidence from such studies must be considered carefully in order to distinguish those substances that are varying as a result of the clock's control over physiological processes from those that may be the mediators of this control. Evidence for a role as mediator would be obtained only if addition of this substance were shown to affect timekeeping, producing either a change in the period or phase.

The state of the art at the present time, then, may be summarized as follows: Many—perhaps most—cells possess a mechanism for measuring time, and this property is shown most clearly by the common occurrence of rhythms within a period of approximately twenty-four hours in constant light and temperature. The biochemistry of this clock is completely unknown. It appears to run autonomously without reference to external time cues and can be reset by changes in light and temperature. The timekeeping shows remarkable insensitivity to light intensity, to temperature, and to various metabolically active substances. The timekeeping mechanism is not intimately connected to gene or nuclear function, but can operate in the cytoplasm in the absence of a nucleus. The problem of the mechanism of biological timekeeping is one of the most challenging to biology at the present time.

REFERENCES

ASCHOFF, J., ed. *Circadian Clocks.* Amsterdam: North-Holland Publishing Co., 1965. 479 pp.

BUNNING, E. *The Physiological Clock; Endogenous Diurnal Rhythms and Biological Chronometry.* Berlin: Springer-Verlag, 1964. 145 pp.

COLD SPRING HARBOR SYMPOSIA ON QUANTITATIVE BIOLOGY. *Biological Clocks.* Vol. 25 (1960). 524 pp.

KARAKASHIAN, M. W., AND J. W. HASTINGS. "The Inhibition of a Biological Clock by Actinomycin D." *Proceedings of the Natural Academy of Science,* Vol. 48 (1962), pp. 2130–2137.

NANDA, K. K., AND K. C. HAMNER. "Studies on the Nature of the Endogenous Rhythm Affecting Photoperiodic Response of Biloxi Soybean." *Botanical Gazette,* Vol. 120 (1958), pp. 14–25.

SWEENEY, B. M. "Biological Clocks in Plants." *Annual Review of Plant Physiology,* Vol. 14 (1963), pp. 411–440.

———, AND F. T. HAXO. "Persistence of a Photosynthetic Rhythm in Enucleated *Acetabularia.*" *Science,* Vol. 134 (1961), pp. 1361–1363.

WILKINS, M. B. "An Endogenous Rhythm in the Rate of Carbon Dioxide Output of Bryophyllum: I, Some Preliminary Experiments." *Journal of Experimental Botany,* Vol. 10 (1959), pp. 377–390.

5

TRANSLOCATION: THE MOVEMENT OF DISSOLVED SUBSTANCES IN PLANTS

Frank B. Salisbury

Utah State University

From the preceding articles it should be quite evident that the higher plant is a very dynamic entity. All kinds of intricate and complex organic molecules are taking part in a great many involved and integrated chemical reactions, the result of which is the complex functioning organism we observe. Yet to think of all this activity, we must imagine entities on the size scale of molecules. In the last article we encountered movements of leaves and other plant parts large enough to see with the unaided eye, and growth is a process of this magnitude, although too slow to be noticeable. In this article we shall discuss a dynamic aspect of the functioning plant that also occurs on a size scale and at rates that could be observed directly: the movements of fluids with their dissolved materials throughout the plant. These movements *could* be observed—that is, if they did not take place inside the plant where they are anything but readily apparent.

The movement of dissolved substances is dependent upon an extensive system of conduits, some living and some dead, all of them integrated in their function in such a way that they enable life processes to continue. The picture of the Cyclamen in Fig. 5–1 may help the reader realize to some extent the intricacy and beauty of this structure. Notice the plant body with its leaves, petioles, and flowers, and notice particularly in the leaves the network of veins containing the conducting system.

The rate of movement occurs at speeds that could be noticed with the unaided eye. Figures 5–2, 5–3, and 5–4 illustrate the magnitude of this movement within the plant. Of the dissolved substances translocated from one part of a plant to another, the flowering hormone may move the most slowly. It is synthesized in the leaf (of a cocklebur plant, for example, which has been subjected to a period of uninterrupted darkness lasting for nine hours or more). The hormone then moves out through the leaf petiole, to the stem tip, thus causing it to produce a flower. Figure 5–2 indicates that this substance moves at the rate of

FIG. 5–1. Cyclamen plant *(Cyclamen persica).*

about 6 to 10 cm per day, which is about the speed of the tip of the hour hand on a wrist watch. Such a velocity would not be obvious, unless one noted the position at one time and then came back sometime later.

Most translocation studies have been concerned with the movement of sugars produced in photosynthesis. Figure 5–3 indicates that their rate of movement, 20 to 100 cm per hour,* is about as fast as the tip of the minute hand on a clock 12 inches in diameter. This would be quite noticeable, as one may see

---

* It is not uncommon to measure rates as high as 150 cm per hour in some plants.

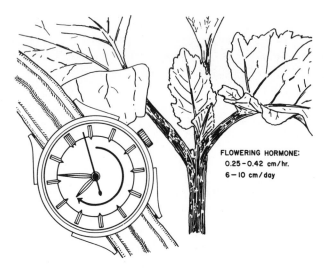

FIG. 5–2. Translocation rates of flowering hormone in the cocklebur plant *(Xanthium pennsylvanicum)*.

FIG. 5–3. Translocation rates of sucrose in phloem tissues of the velvetplant *(Gynura aurantiaca)*.

for himself by watching closely the minute hand on a clock about that size. The rate of water movement upward through the dead xylem elements of a tree trunk may vary from a standstill (during periods of rain, for example) to rates of 50 to 4,360 cm per hour, depending upon the species and environmental conditions. The maximum rate given in Fig. 5–4 is as fast as the tip of a sweep second hand on a clock 9½ inches in diameter!

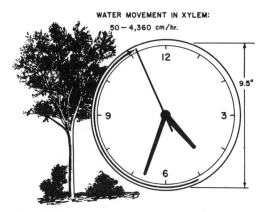

WATER MOVEMENT IN XYLEM:
50 — 4,360 cm/hr.

FIG. 5–4. Rate of movement of water in xylem tissues of trees.

What is the cause of movement in these examples? Within the plant, or for that matter in any situation where fluids are transported, movement occurs in response to either or both of two kinds of force gradients. First, there are hydrostatic gradients. This kind of force gradient is established in any pumping system, such as the heart. One of the principal theories to be discussed here postulates that translocation in plants occurs in response to such a pressure gradient.

The other kind of force gradient, resulting in movement of individual molecules, is more subtle and could involve considerable discussion and definition. We shall review it briefly. This is a gradient in partial molar free energies which we shall refer to simply as free energy. Such a gradient results in movement by diffusion, the molecules moving from points of high free energy to points of low free energy. In the familiar example of osmosis, free energy of the water may be less on one side of a membrane than on the other, due to the presence of some material dissolved in the water (a solute). Thus water will tend to diffuse across the membrane toward the point of lower free energy. The solute has a much higher free energy on one side of the membrane than on the other, but since it cannot pass through the membrane, this difference is maintained. Increasing pressure will increase the free energy. For a given amount of solute, a specific pressure is required to raise the free energy of water in the solution to the level of pure water at atmospheric pressure.

The osmotic potential, a property of any solution, may be expressed in pressure terms that are equivalent to this pressure. For example, a 5.0 percent solution of sugar has an osmotic potential of about 8.5 atmospheres. That is, about 8.5 Atm (130 lbs/in^2) of pressure on the solution are required to keep pure water from entering it through a semipermeable membrane.

In the plant, either kind of force gradient may come about in response to environmental conditions (for example, an abundance of water in the soil with very little in the atmosphere) and in response to metabolic processes taking place within the plant.

SOME ASPECTS OF PLANT STRUCTURE RELATING TO TRANSLOCATION

We cannot at this point digress into a detailed discussion of plant anatomy. Yet we must review a few basic principles. The plant body consists of roots, stems, leaves, and special organs such as flowers and fruits. Carbohydrates and other compounds are synthesized in the leaves, and they must be moved to the roots and to the developing fruits and other parts of the plant. Movement occurs through the vascular system, consisting of phloem elements and xylem elements. The phloem occurs in the bark, while the xylem constitutes the wood in stems and roots of most perennials, consisting primarily of dead cells. Movement of sugars takes place primarily in the phloem tissues, while water with its dissolved minerals moves up through the plant from the soil to the leaves primarily via the xylem tissues.

Figure 5–5 is a schematic representation of a root cross section. Some of the

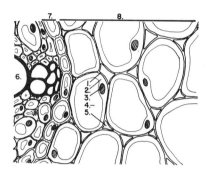

FIG. 5–5. Portion of a cross section through a young buttercup (*Ranunculus*) root (schematic): (1) cell wall; (2) cytoplasm; (3) nucleus; (4) vacuole; (5) intercellular space; (6) a large xylem element; (7) the endodermal layer surrounding the stele; (8) cortex.

cell features are labeled to help in orientation. Number 6 refers to the open lumen or cavity of a xylem vessel. Number 7 points out the layer of cells between the outer cortex (number 8) and the inner vascular elements making up the stele. This layer of cells (number 7) is called the endodermis. Between number 6 and number 7 are the living cells that represent the developing phloem elements. The vascular cylinder surrounded by the endodermis is called the stele.

We may regard the cellular plant body as consisting primarily of two phases, as illustrated in Fig. 5–6 and 5–7. Figure 5–6 shows the cell walls and intercellular spaces of Fig. 5–5 blackened with all of the living part of the tissue omitted. The system of interconnected cell walls may be referred to as the apoplast. We might imagine that water with its dissolved substances could freely diffuse throughout the apoplast and those intercellular spaces filled with water. The water-filled lumens of the xylem elements would also be part of this system. If water and dissolved substances can readily diffuse throughout this system and

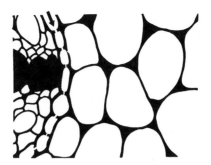

FIG. 5–6. The apoplast and intercellular spaces of Fig. 5–5. The apoplast proper includes only the system of cell walls, and the break indicated at the endodermal layer is not a break in the apoplast, but a break in the free space due to the relative impermeability of the Casparian strips to water.

less readily into the living part of the plant, then this system would be equivalent to the part of the plant that has been called the free space. Note in Fig. 5–6 that there is an interruption in the free space along the row of endodermal cells, although this is not a break in the apoplast itself. It comes about because of a strip of relatively waterproof, suberized material around each endodermal cell (the Casparian strip). Thus substances diffusing through the apoplast from the outside cannot pass into the stele via the apoplast, but must pass through the living endodermal cells (cytoplasm and perhaps vacuole).

Figure 5–7 shows the cytoplasm and nuclei of the cells in Fig. 5–5, the continuous living phase of the plant called the symplast. The cytoplasm is connected from cell to cell by strands passing through minute pores in the cell wall. These continuous protoplasmic connections between cells, called plasmodesmata, have now been seen with the electron microscope in a wide variety of plant tissues. Thus we might imagine that substances in the cytoplasm of one cell could move to the cytoplasm of other cells without ever entering into the apoplast system. They would move only through the symplast. The arrows in Fig. 5–7 indicate that the cytoplasm may stream, exhibiting a movement called cyclosis. This movement is easy to watch in certain systems and is probably widespread in plant cells. Such streaming would tend greatly to accelerate the movement of dissolved materials throughout the symplast.

The vacuole, as shown in Fig. 5–7, is surrounded by a membrane capable of retaining dissolved substances in the vacuole even though their concentration is much higher than it is outside. This membrane has been referred to as the tonoplast, and in our apoplast-symplast terminology it is called the endoplast. The cytoplasm itself along with the nuclei and other bodies constitute the mesoplasm, while the membrane surrounding the cytoplasm of each cell may be called the ectoplast.

Figure 5–8 shows schematically the development and maturation of a phloem-

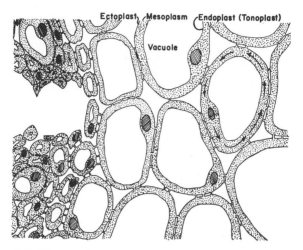

FIG. 5–7. The symplast or "living portion" of Fig. 5–5. Note the arrows indicating cytoplasmic streaming in one cell.

tube element consisting of a sieve tube (the large cell) and the companion cells found in association with the sieve tubes. The young phloem element (A) is not much different from other young undifferentiated cells. It contains a large visible nucleus, considerable cytoplasm, and obvious vacuoles. The long arrows indicate that cytoplasmic streaming may be observed. As the cell matures (B), the nucleus begins to disappear; so-called slime bodies appear in the cytoplasm, and the cytoplasmic streaming is less active. The mature sieve tube element (C) lacks a nucleus, and the demarcation between cytoplasm and vacuole (the tonoplast) is no longer readily apparent. The slime bodies have essentially disintegrated, but their remains can often be observed. The ends of the sieve tube elements consist of sieve plates. A cross section through one of these plates (D) indicates that cytoplasm passes from cell to cell through pores. Whether or not the vacuole is also continuous between cells through the sieve plates is not apparent, but the best and most recent electronmicrographs indicate more and more clearly that fluids could flow rather readily through the sieve plates.

ROOT PRESSURES AND EXUDATES

If one cuts off the top of a plant, especially an herbaceous one or a vine such as grape, material will sometimes be exuded under considerable pressure from the cut surface. The concentration of dissolved substances in the exuded sap is much higher than that of the soil solution (or nutrient culture solution in an artificial situation). The idea of higher concentrations of minerals inside a cell compared to those outside is not new: the process referred to as accumulation or active uptake uses metabolic energy to move substances across a membrane against a concentration gradient, so that the concentration on one side

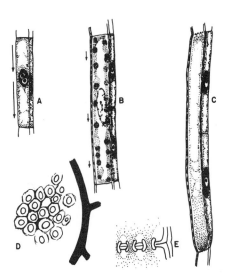

FIG. 5–8. Some morphological aspects of sieve tubes. (A) Young sieve tube element with companion cells. Long arrows indicate considerable cytoplasmic streaming. (B) Sieve tube of intermediate maturity. Slime bodies are evident, the nucleus is beginning to disappear, and cytoplasmic streaming is no longer readily evident. (C) Mature sieve tube element. The nucleus, endoplast, and cytoplasmic streaming are no longer evident. (D) Cross section through a sieve tube near the sieve plate, showing pores. (E) Longitudinal section of sieve tube through a sieve plate, showing cytoplasmic connections through the pores. [After Katherine Esau, *Plant Anatomy* (1953). By permission of John Wiley & Sons.]

may build up much above that on the other side. This phenomenon has been studied in considerable detail for many years by a number of plant physiologists.

But how does this work with a whole plant instead of just an individual cell? The apoplast-symplast concept, along with our understanding of the endodermal layer and its impermeable Casparian strips, helps us to formulate a mechanism to account for the observed phenomenon. This was done by Crafts and Broyer in 1938. They postulated that dissolved salts from the soil solution move into the plant primarily by diffusion through the apoplast of the cortex. The symplast then accumulates these ions actively by its metabolic processes, moving the ions across the ectoplast (outer membrane). Since there is an ample amount of available oxygen in the cells nearest the surface, these cells tend metabolically to accumulate ions to high concentrations. These materials then move via the symplast (undoubtedly aided by cytoplasmic streaming) toward the inside of the root. They have no difficulty in moving across the endodermal cells, because these cells are part of the symplast. Once these materials are inside the stele, oxygen tensions are much lower and the processes of accumulation are much less efficient. The substances then begin to leak out into the surrounding apoplast and into the water-filled xylem tubes. Thus we can see how concentrations might be built up inside the stele above those outside of the root.

Such an increase in concentration would then put into effect the process of osmosis, with the endodermal layer of cells acting as the semipermeable membrane of an osmometer. Water would move in through the outer apoplast, through the endodermis, and finally into the apoplast within the stele. This would create pressure as in any osmometer, and if the stem is cut, the pressure will be made manifest by a root pressure exudate.

Thus our concept of structure allows us to account for root pressure. Yet root pressures cannot always be observed. We would expect to find them only under conditions in which water accumulating inside the stele has no place to go, resulting in a buildup of pressures.

WATER UPTAKE BY COHESION

If water is evaporating from the leaves at a fairly rapid rate, we would not expect root pressures to develop at all. And usually they do not. In the absence of root pressures the plant seems to act simply as a water conduit between the soil and the air; water flows down the free-energy gradient, so to speak. The actual movement of water through the stem is in response to hydraulic gradients, but these in turn are established by the free-energy gradient. The plant is acting like a wick.

Water flowing through the plant conduit will carry dissolved minerals from the soil with it. It is noteworthy that the amount of dissolved minerals is not a direct function of the rate at which water is moving through the plant— probably because the minerals must move through the endodermal layer in the symplast rather than the apoplast, and hence there is some metabolic control of mineral uptake.

Figure 5–9 illustrates this movement of water. In a soil that is wet nearly to field capacity, the osmotic potential of the soil solution is very low; and, if there is no pressure, this osmotic potential will be equal to the so-called diffusion pressure deficit* (DPD) (about 0.1 atmosphere in Fig. 5–9). When the diffusion pressure deficit is extremely low, the free energy of the water is relatively high. The osmotic potential of root cells has been found to be between 5 and 6 atmospheres. If the root cells are not under pressure the DPD would be 5 to 6 atmospheres, and the free energy would be lower than in the surrounding soil water. Free energies are still lower in leaf cells where DPDs may be 10 to 50 atmospheres (ignoring pressures), and the free energy of water in the atmosphere is much lower. In air† at 90 percent relative humidity and 20°C temperature,

---

* The diffusion pressure deficit (DPD) is equal to the osmotic potential minus the pressure and expresses, therefore, the net tendency for pure water at atmospheric pressure to diffuse into the area to which the DPD refers.

† The air has no osmotic potential in a strict sense, and free energies are difficult to express, hence the use of diffusion pressure deficit.

SOME QUANTITIES RELATING TO WATER IN
ITS SOIL–PLANT–AIR PATHWAY

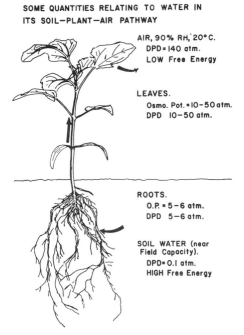

AIR, 90% RH, 20°C.
DPD = 140 atm.
LOW Free Energy

LEAVES.
Osmo. Pot. = 10–50 atm.
DPD 10–50 atm.

ROOTS.
O.P. = 5–6 atm.
DPD 5–6 atm.

SOIL WATER (near
Field Capacity).
DPD = 0.1 atm.
HIGH Free Energy

FIG. 5–9. The plant as a water conduit between the soil and the air.

the DPD is 140 atmospheres, and air with a relative humidity of 40 percent contains water having a DPD of 1,220 atmospheres at 20°C. Thus there is a steep gradient from low to high DPD and from high to low free energy, going from the soil water through the plant into the atmosphere.

So water will evaporate readily from the leaf surfaces. As water is removed from the leaf, it will be pulled up in the xylem elements. Rather high tensions may be developed in holding the column of water together between the roots and the leaves. In a tall tree we can easily calculate that tensions of at least −20 atmospheres must be developed. Why don't such extreme tensions cause the water to cavitate? That is, why don't bubbles of water vapor form under these conditions, causing the columns to break? Probably cavitation usually fails because of the extremely small dimensions of the xylem elements (from 15 to 500 microns in diameter). This has been demonstrated with small capillary tubes in a centrifuge where it is possible artificially to impose such high tensions in a liquid.

There are many unsolved problems in this field. What happens, for example, when water does cavitate in the xylem tubes? This might be expected to happen during a strong windstorm, and probably it happens every winter in trees that freeze, since freezing forces dissolved air out of the water. Microscopic examination has demonstrated that the xylem elements do contain an abundance of air bubbles after having been frozen. The columns may be restored during a rain storm when water is absorbed by the leaves, moving downward toward the roots. Or perhaps, as present evidence seems to indicate, the tree has a superabundance of xylem columns and can do without most of them! New water-filled ones are being made as the trunk grows in diameter.

The remaining problems will be solved with techniques and knowledge developed by hydraulic engineers in their study of water movement through confined spaces, such as in the soil. Probably the greatest single advance might be the development of some means for measuring negative pressures (tensions) in liquids, especially within a plant. So far, we are left almost exclusively with our calculations and with certain indirect experimental approaches. The area could be a fruitful one for graduate students with suitable inclinations in the physical sciences.

THE MOVEMENT OF ASSIMILATES

As mentioned earlier, the main organic constituent moved in solution throughout the plant is sugar. Of course, amino acids also move with the plant, as do various hormones and even substances as complex as protein (for example, virus particles are known to move within the plant).

We can begin our discussion of sugar translocation with the basic information that movement takes place in a direction from point of origin (source) to point of utilization (sink). The point of origin is usually a photosynthesizing cell, but it could also be a cell that is converting insoluble starch to soluble sugar. The point of utilization can be any cell using sugar in a metabolic process such as respiration, or storing it as starch. These nonphotosynthesizing cells occur in the roots, in the cortex, the pith rays, the lateral and terminal meristems, the flowers, and the fruits.

Two principal mechanisms are being considered to account for movement of sugars throughout the plant. Substances move from source to sink by diffusion, but this is a very slow process, and mechanisms must be devised to increase the rates. The cytoplasmic-streaming hypothesis illustrated in Fig. 5–10 is an example of such a mechanism. The idea is that rates are accounted for by cytoplasmic streaming, but diffusion plays a role in moving materials from one cell to the adjacent cell. We have already considered the process in discussing movement of dissolved substances through the symplast from the outer surfaces of the root into the stele. Figure 5–10 illustrates cytoplasmic streaming where two sieve tube elements join at the sieve plate. The black dots represent one substance in high concentration, and the white dots represent another substance in lower concentration, but moving in the opposite direction. Such a mechanism would permit movement in both directions, always from the source to the sink of the particular substance being translocated. It is an attractive mechanism, but it is untenable for mature sieve tubes, simply because the cytoplasm does not stream in these phloem cells. Yet we can imagine that this mechanism may play a role

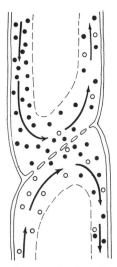

FIG. 5–10. The cytoplasmic-streaming hypothesis of solute translocation.

in any instance where the cytoplasm does stream, such as in cortical cells, photosynthesizing cells in the leaf, and young sieve tube elements.

Currently scientists, especially in Great Britain, are excited by a theory of R. Thaine which holds that strands of cytoplasm move along through the sieve tubes and the sieve plates in response to some sort of metabolic activity. Moving pictures purporting to show the effect are unconvincing, however, and even if their interpretation could be accepted at face value, the rates are far too slow to agree with those discussed below.

The other approach suggests that assimilates move through the sieve tube elements in a bulk flow of material. The mechanism that might create this mass flow is demonstrated by the model in Fig. 5–11, which was suggested by the German plant physiologist Münch in 1930. Two osmometers are connected by a tube, and both are surrounded by water. One osmometer contains a high concentration of solute, while the other contains a much more dilute solution. The concentration of substances in the water surrounding the osmometers is low in comparison with the concentration inside. The osmometer containing the concentrated solution will take up water by osmosis, developing a pressure. This pressure will be transmitted to the other osmometer (with the speed of sound). In the second osmometer, where the concentration is low and the free energy relatively high, the pressure arriving from the first osmometer will tend to increase the free energy until it is above that of the surrounding solution. Thus water will diffuse out of the second osmometer, resulting in a flow of material from the first osmometer to the second; and anything dissolved in this material will simply be carried along in a bulk flow. The pressure could also be

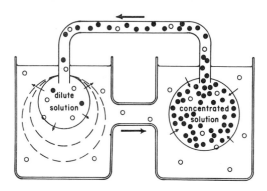

FIG. 5–11. A model illustrating the pressure-flow theory of solute translocation as proposed by Münch.

relieved by expansion of the second osmometer, rather than by movement of material out of it. This expansion—which might be the case in the growth of a fruit, for example—is indicated by the broken lines in Fig. 5–11. The black dots indicate the main osmotic component (for example, sugar), and the open circles represent another dissolved substance present at a much lower concentration. This second substance would simply move along with the first, and if it could pass through the membranes it might even circulate throughout the system.

Figure 5–12 illustrates Münch's pressure-flow hypothesis as applied to the plant. The right-hand osmometer of Fig. 5–11 is analogous to a producer cell of Fig. 5–12 where osmotic potential is maintained high. The consumer cell, where sugars are continuously being removed by respiration and other processes, represents the left osmometer. The phloem elements (the symplast as a whole) represent the connecting link between the two osmometers, and the surrounding solution occurs in the apoplast. Arrows indicate the direction of motion in the system. We should note that the plant system may never reach equilibrium because sugars are continually being produced and used up, whereas the physical model of Münch will reach equilibrium when enough material has been moved from the first osmometer to the second to make the concentrations equal in both.

How can we test the mechanism of Münch in the plant? The following statement seems logical: If there is an osmotic gradient, if there is a pressure gradient, and if flow through sieve tubes can occur, then the pressure-flow mechanism must exist in the plant. This is not to imply that the existence of such a mechanism would eliminate any other sort of mechanism.

The presence of an osmotic gradient was indicated in Fig. 5–9. Osmotic potentials in leaf cells are considerably higher than they are in root cells. Zimmermann in 1957 made careful measurements of osmotic potentials at different heights along the trunk of an ash tree. He collected material from phloem cells

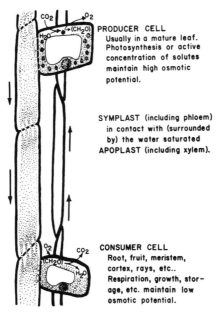

PRODUCER CELL
Usually in a mature leaf.
Photosynthesis or active
concentration of solutes
maintain high osmotic
potential.

SYMPLAST (including phloem)
in contact with (surrounded
by) the water saturated
APOPLAST (including xylem).

CONSUMER CELL
Root, fruit, meristem,
cortex, rays, etc..
Respiration, growth, storage, etc. maintain low
osmotic potential.

FIG. 5–12. The pressure-flow theory of Münch as it is applied to the plant.

and analyzed it for a number of sugars. The osmotic (concentration) gradient is apparent from his results, shown in Fig. 5–13. The presence of an osmotic

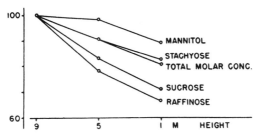

FIG. 5–13. Relative concentration of sugars in phloem exudate from white ash (*Fraxinus americana*), shown as a function of height above the base of the tree. Decreasing osmotic potential with decreasing height is evident.

gradient implies a pressure gradient, but this is much more difficult to measure, and a gradient in pressures has not yet been conclusively demonstrated. As we shall see, the material in the sieve tube elements is under pressure, so that we are probably not going too far astray to admit that pressure gradients do occur. The remaining question, then, concerns whether or not substances will flow through the sieve tube elements.

There is a considerable body of literature relating to this problem. For many years studies have been made in which phloem tissue is carefully cut and sap is seen to exude from it. Indeed, there are instances when phloem exudate is of commercial importance. The sugar palm (*Phoenix dactylifera*), for example, may exude 10 liters of sap a day. The Palmyra palm in India (*Borassus flabel-lider*) may exude 11 liters of sap per day, and this sap may contain as high as 10 percent sucrose with 0.25 percent of dissolved mineral solutes. The flow in such cases may be as rapid as 100 to 500 cm per hour through the sieve tubes. Since this is faster than the normal rate of flow in the intact plant, we might assume that relieving the pressure by cutting into the phloem elements results in a more rapid flow.

In recent years these studies have been greatly refined and extended by the use of "phloem-sucking" insects. Certain aphids insert their stylets directly and selectively into the sieve tube elements of the phloem. Sap is then forced into their bodies by the pressure in the sieve tube elements (they exert no active sucking processes themselves). Exudate even collects on the surface of their bodies where it is in turn consumed by ants. In recent studies, the aphid was allowed to insert the stylet into the phloem; and then the insect was cut off, leaving the stylet in the phloem. Sap exuded from the cut stylet for a considerable period of time (days in some instances). In a case where rate of movement was about 100 cm per hour, it was calculated that the contents of one hundred sieve tube elements must be emptied each minute. Thus the entire contents of each sieve tube must move through the sieve plate in less than a second (far too rapidly to be accounted for by Thaine's hypothesis).

Much of this work has been directed toward analysis of the phloem exudate. We will not discuss this aspect of the problem, except to state that results are "logical"—that is, they are what one might expect if assimilates are being actively moved through the phloem conducting system.

The important point is that bulk flow does occur through sieve tubes. We might ask ourselves about the importance of lateral movement through the side walls of sieve tube elements. It has been shown that the sieve tube elements can be plasmolyzed, which indicates that the membrane surrounding the elements is much less permeable to solutes than are the ends of the sieve tube elements through which bulk flow of material passes. It might be concluded, then, that longitudinal movement is much more important than lateral movement. Nevertheless, lateral movement has often been demonstrated (for example, by the use of radioactive tracers). This movement would be expected on the basis of the symplast concept. If there are consuming cells in the neighborhood of a sieve tube element (such as phloem parenchyma, rays, cortex, or pith cells), then lateral movement would be a natural result of the phloem's role as a distribution system.

We have not met all of the conditions established above, and so it must be concluded that a pressure-flow mechanism operates within the plant.

How important is such a mechanism in the overall translocation of organic solutes? If natural and applied solutes move in the plant along with the sugar (the main osmotic component), then we might feel that the mass-flow mechanism is indeed an important one. If, on the other hand, substances move strictly according to their own concentration gradients (as might be accounted for by cytoplasmic streaming—see Fig. 5–10), then we would be tempted to conclude that pressure flow is important only under certain conditions.

A great deal of research extending over the last three decades seems to lead to the conclusion that substances nearly always move in the same direction in the phloem. Early work in the 1930s involving the movement of plant viruses was extensive and impressive. More recently a considerable amount of work has utilized the weed killer 2,4-D. Since this compound causes bending and other visible responses in the plant, one can easily apply it to one site and subsequently know where it ends up in the plant. In a great many experiments performed over the past fifteen years, it has been shown that 2,4-D always follows the movement of sugar. If 2,4-D is applied to a leaf that has been darkened for a period of time, it will not move out until the leaf has either been allowed to photosynthesize or has been treated externally with sugar. Nor will 2,4-D move into a leaf that is exporting sugar.

More recently, this basic conclusion has been reinforced by the use of many radioactive minerals and organic molecules—various growth regulators, antibiotics, and so forth. Sometimes such molecules will even move against their own concentration gradient, as long as they are moving with the sugar. Other experiments have shown that radioactive water (using tritium) and labeled solutes move together in the same direction. In some of these instances, any sort of accelerated diffusion mechanism such as cytoplasmic streaming simply does not account for the observed results. We may conclude, then, that since diverse substances follow a mass-flow pattern, Münch's pressure-flow mechanism must be important in the plant.

How do rates of movement agree with the pressure-flow mechanism (or any mechanism for that matter)? This is the one problem still remaining for the understanding of plant translocation. Rates are simply too fast to be easily accounted for by present theories. If we consider that maximum rates are 150 cm per hour, as in the ash tree, and then take into account the fact that the sieve plate openings make up only about one eleventh of the overall cross-sectional area of the sieve tube, then we must conclude that substances move through these openings at the rate of 16.5 meters per hour. This seems a phenomenal rate for openings that are so small. And it should be remembered that in cut phloem the rate may be many times faster than this. Such extreme rates often result in plugging of the sieve tube plates, probably by dislodging materials to produce the so-called slime plugs. Nevertheless, the flow does occur; and so we are simply left with the problem of understanding how it can happen.

A number of studies have shown that the sieve tube elements are functional only when they are alive and metabolizing. If they are killed, or respiration is inhibited in any way, movement through them ceases. Since Münch's model will not help us understand this requirement for metabolism, what does it all mean? We remind ourselves that phloem cells seem quite different from other plant cells. The nucleus is gone, the endoplast is indistinct or missing, and companion cells are present. Certain attempts to measure respiration rates have indicated that they are different when phloem and other cells are compared. What does all this have to do with translocation?

These are the important problems awaiting solution. We need to study the physiology of phloem cells, but it seems impossible to get at them without disturbing their function. We are at least making a careful examination of sieve tubes and plates with the electron microscope, and knowledge about their submicroscopic structure is beginning to contribute to our understanding of their function. Crafts has speculated that the surrounding cytoplasm in the sieve plate pores somehow causes water to be in a superfluid condition (water molecules ordered in such a way that they flow with virtually no viscosity). Could we relate such a possibility to metabolism? The concept of the accumulation of substances into the sieve tube elements will probably eventually be a part of our thinking, and "activated diffusion" (related to metabolism) across the sieve plates has often been suggested. So far, however, there is no convincing evidence.

For many years botanists have also wondered about the effects of temperature upon assimilate translocation. Some studies have indicated that, for a given temperature range, translocation increases as temperature decreases. This indeed would be surprising; and, to complicate the picture, we have equally reliable reports that temperature effects upon translocation are just the opposite—that increasing temperature results in increasing translocation. This is a field badly in need of clarification. Some of these experiments were done with whole plants; others were done simply by cooling the petiole with a water jacket. Perhaps both methods should be combined within a single research program to resolve the apparent paradox.

The report that bidirectional movement will sometimes occur in the phloem elements has for many years been a source of confusion. If it could be shown that one substance moves in one direction in a given phloem sieve tube while another substance is moving in the opposite direction, Münch's pressure-flow mechanism would not be applicable. Though actually this has never been rigorously demonstrated, there is nevertheless considerable evidence for bidirectional movement within a single vascular bundle.

Much past work on bidirectional movement utilized dyes, but Biddulph and Cory of Washington State University have approached the problem with considerable elegance by using radioactive tracers. They applied labeled carbon dioxide to an upper leaf on a bean plant; the carbon dioxide was subsequently incorporated into radioactive sugar. They then applied labeled phosphorus as phosphate to the leaf immediately below the one treated with radioactive carbon dioxide. The position of the phosphorus could then be determined on a radio-autograph by shielding out the weak rays from the carbon. After many months the phosphorus had decayed away, and the position of the carbon was determined. In a majority of trials Biddulph and Cory found bidirectional movement of these two substances. In some cases the bidirectional movement took place in separate bundles; Münch's pressure-flow mechanism could always be used to explain these cases. Sometimes, however, bidirectional movement occurred in the same bundle; and, when the two substances could be resolved, movement appeared to occur within the same phloem elements.

In the latter cases, Biddulph and Cory were able to locate the bidirectional movement in young phloem tissue (which is exactly where we might expect such an occurrence, since cytoplasm is still known to stream in these immature phloem elements). Their conclusion was that both mechanisms must operate in the bean plant. Since there is no apparent reason to believe that both mechanisms do *not* operate, we must not eliminate cytoplasmic-streaming mechanisms from our thinking just because we accept pressure-flow mechanisms. If the cytoplasm streams, and if diffusion will occur from cytoplasm to cytoplasm in adjacent cells, then the mechanism must operate.

OTHER TOPICS RELATING TO TRANSLOCATION
OF DISSOLVED SUBSTANCES

As should be apparent by now, the field of translocation is indeed a broad one, and there are still many aspects that we cannot consider in detail. However, because many of them are quite interesting, we shall devote a paragraph to each of eight topics.

1. *Differences in mobility of substances within the plant.* Some substances appear to be extremely mobile within the plant, whereas others are comparatively immobile. Phosphorus, potassium, sodium, chlorine, sulfur, and some nitrogen compounds are quite mobile. On the other hand, calcium, magnesium, iron, and cobalt, which seem to be bound in plant tissue, are essentially immobile after they arrive in the leaf via the transpiration stream. Considerable work has been done using various weed killers and other growth regulators. One study utilized small cubes of potato tissue. Radioactive compounds were applied to a spot on these cubes, and after a period of time the position of the substances was determined. It was found that 2,4-D, indole acetic acid, amitrol, and maleic hydrazide form a mobility series in the cytoplasm, in which 2,4-D is least mobile and maleic hydrazide is most mobile. The compound monuron failed to move in the cytoplasm, but diffused readily throughout the potato tissue through the apoplast. These different mobilities remind us of a chromatogram, in which compounds are separated from one another by their solubility in a solvent and by the tenacity with which they adhere to another material such as filter paper. Surely some substances are more soluble in the liquid of cytoplasm or sieve tube elements, and some would be more tenaciously adsorbed by the

protein and cell-wall materials of tissues. Such an approach should readily account for differences in mobility.

2. *Free circulation of substances in the plant.* In sugar cane, radioactive phosphorus will move out of the treated leaf through the phloem system into the root, back into the apoplast, up through the xylem, into the leaf, and around and around a number of times. Potassium, sulphate, maleic hydrazide, and probably dalapon are equally capable of circulation within the plant. Russian workers have reported that even sugar will circulate in this fashion. Iron and zinc may circulate if the acidity is high and the phosphorus content is low. Otherwise these substances appear to be precipitated out as phosphates and become immobile. Calcium, magnesium, and cobalt apparently will not circulate under any conditions. All of this is interesting from a historical standpoint. William Harvey's discovery of circulation in animals was followed by a search for an equivalent circulation in plants; because plants have no pumping organ comparable to the heart, early scientists concluded that such a circulation in plants does not exist. However, it has since been discovered that if individual substances are considered, circulation of a sort does take place. This finding seems important when we recall that substances may be moved out of a leaf before the leaf dies and falls off in the autumn. If removal from the leaf is related to circulation, then we have a phenomenon of importance to the nutrition of the plant.

3. *Movement of gases through the plant's intercellular-space system.*   C. D. Nelson of Canada reports that gases may move from the upper parts of the plant down to the roots at rates as high as 50 meters per hour or even higher. This movement might occur through the gas-filled intercellular spaces of a plant (which may make up as much as 20 percent by volume of a land plant and 70 percent or more in certain aquatic stems).

4. *Alpha-methoxyphenylacetic acid secreted by roots.*   Researchers at Beltsville, Maryland, found that when this compound is applied to the tops of various plants, it will subsequently collect in the nutrient medium around the roots and then be absorbed by neighboring plants having intermingling root systems. An important aspect of this finding is that secretion from the roots depends upon metabolic activity and is not simply a leakage through the apoplast system. Obviously, the discovery might be important in agriculture, if it could be applied to specific compounds such as those capable of controlling pathogens in the soil. It would then be necessary only to spray the chemical on the mature crop and expect it to end up finely distributed in the soil. The finding is also of ecological importance, because substances secreted by one plant may be inhibitory to the growth of another.

5. *Translocated heat injury.*   A rather recent paper reports that when one leaf suffers heat injury, in a very few seconds other leaves will show the same symptoms. The transport mechanisms involved in this phenomenon seem to be quite different from those we have emphasized here.

6. *Polar transport.*   Growth regulators that cause the elongation of plant

cells may be made in the shoot tip and then moved downward where control of stem growth is attained. Interestingly enough, these compounds will move only in that direction; for if a section of stem is removed and inverted, and a source of this compound placed on top, movement to the bottom will not occur unless the concentration is much higher than that normally found in the plant. It even has been reported that sugars will move only in a polar direction out of a leaf. Such polar movement is presently a complete mystery, although it seems to imply that the cell is distinctly different from one end to the other, and that this difference will result in very specific functional phenomena such as control in direction of movement. The whole finding points up aspects of the translocation problem that have scarcely been considered.

7. *Movement of flowering hormone.* As indicated previously, the flowering hormone moves at an exceptionally slow rate. What does this imply about translocation? Might this slow rate represent a separate class of substances? Can we infer anything about the nature of the flowering hormone from this finding? In the past it has been suggested that the flowering hormone is an exceptionally large molecule, though the meager evidence probably does not justify this conclusion.

8. *Movement of the excitation stimulus in Mimosa.* The series of photographs shown in Fig. 5–14 illustrates an interesting phenomenon that we still fail to understand. The sensitive plant *Mimosa pudica* folds up its leaflets and its leaves upon contact. If one touches the plant with some object, it is likely that the whole plant will be disturbed and all its leaves and leaflets will fold up almost at once. If, however, one is extremely careful to contact only a portion of the plant (this may be done using a flame as in Fig. 5–14), then the folding up progresses from the point of contact back through the plant body. Since there is no evidence of any nervous system in plants, it is assumed this response comes about because some sort of chemical stimulus is translocated from the point of contact, and there is direct evidence that this is the case. The series of photographs in Fig. 5–14 demonstrates the phenomenon and indicates that we might easily notice some activities in higher plants. Eleven seconds after the stimulation by the flame, most of the leaflets had folded up on the one branch that was contacted. Eleven seconds later, the stimulus had moved into other branches; and by the end of the sixty-second interval, all parts of the plant within the area of the photograph had responded. It would be most interesting to understand the mechanism of such a rapid and spectacular response.

From Fig. 5–15 we are reminded again of the intricate complexity of a mature higher plant and the complex biochemical reactions taking place within each cell. In addition, we can recall the complex distributional system that accounts for movement of dissolved substances throughout the plant; the figure shows that the network of veins extends to every part of the plant leaf, so that this distributional system contacts virtually every cell in the plant. Our comprehensive picture is further improved if we think of the symplast system, through which movement of substances may be accelerated by cytoplasmic stream-

FIG. 5–14. Movement of the excitation stimulus in *Mimosa pudica* after initial contact with flame. Compare the extent of collapse of the leaflets and leaves with the second hand on the clock.

ing and bulk flow through sieve tube elements. Indeed, the entire phloem system may be considered as the distributional phase of the symplast. We may also imagine the more passive diffusional and hydraulic movements of water (with

FIG. 5–15. The velvetplant (*Gynura aurantiaca*).

its many dissolved salts and few organic molecules) through the apoplast, of which the xylem elements must constitute a specialized distributional aspect. Both systems are integrated to provide the higher plant with the machinery for growth, development, and metabolism.

REFERENCES

Annual Review of Plant Physiology. Palo Alto, Calif.: Annual Reviews, Inc. (Technical articles on translocation are reviewed periodically in this annually appearing series.)

BONNER, J. F., AND A. W. GALSTON. *Principles of Plant Physiology.* San Francisco: W. H. Freeman & Company, Publishers, 1952.

CRAFT, A. S. *Translocation in Plants.* New York: Holt, Rinehart and Winston, Inc., 1961.

ESAU, K. *Anatomy of Seed Plants.* New York: John Wiley & Sons, Inc., 1960.

———. *Plant Anatomy.* New York: John Wiley & Sons, Inc., 1964.

GALSTON, A. W. *The Life of the Green Plant.* Englewood Cliffs, N.J.: Prentice-Hall, Inc., 1961.

SALISBURY, F. B., AND R. V. PARKE. *Vascular Plants: Form and Function.* Belmont, Calif.: Wadsworth Publishing Company, Inc., 1964.

Scientific American. (Contains many articles of current botanical interest.)

STEWARD, F. C. *Plants at Work.* Palo Alto, Calif.: Addison-Wesley Publishing Company, Inc., 1964.

BIOCHEMICAL METHODS IN SYSTEMATICS

6

Ralph E. Alston and B. L. Turner

Department of Botany
The University of Texas

As defined by Dr. G. G. Simpson, systematics is the scientific study of the kinds of organisms and all relationships among them. If we accept the spirit of this definition, systematics cannot afford to stay aloof from any major conceptual or technical advance in any field of biology. Thus, the theory of evolution, and advances in genetics, cytology, and ecology have all contributed to systematics in quite fundamental ways. Even biochemistry has been of great importance, though perhaps more subtly. Studies of basic metabolism in the 1930s revealed that the chemical diversity in living organisms concealed a unified substructure through which the origins of the chemical differences might be traced. This unified substructure removed most of the remaining props from anti-Darwinism; and the biochemical story, meeting with eloquent indifference, was integrated with biology-at-large. Botanists such as Gibbs and biochemists such as Florkin have long been aware that chemical data are potentially of great use to systematics as broadly defined, but until recently, really effective techniques for acquiring the right kinds of chemical knowledge were lacking. Fortunately, the upsurge of interest in molecular biology has led to the development of ingenious methods and amazing technical triumphs.

Now that these powerful research tools are available, will taxonomists retreat into an ever-narrowing sphere of influence, sticking close to tradition when other biologists are in the midst of one of the most exciting periods of discovery? Or will taxonomists become adventurous, moving with the mainstream of biological progress? In recent years it has been increasingly evident that many of the methods of chemists and biochemists could be used to advantage by taxonomists—not to erect "new" phylogenetic trees, like *Psilotum,* with beautiful dichotomous branches and shallow intellectual roots—but rather to add a vast number of new facts of special relevance to systematics. Thus, as we shall see later, chemical markers may serve as effectively as cytological markers in the study of population dynamics.

At least three books have been written recently on "chemotaxonomy" or biochemical systematics (two of them by chemists), and several international meetings of chemists and botanists together have attempted to establish a broad operational definition of biochemical systematics and to lay down more effective lines of communication between biologists and chemists. The following account of biochemical systematics is intended to illustrate some present contributions to this field and some possibilities for the future.

Botanists interested in the so-called "higher" plants have a great advantage over most other biologists who might be interested in biochemical systematics, because the flowering plants produce thousands of chemical compounds (Fig. 6–1). Most of these compounds are of uncertain function in the plant, and the

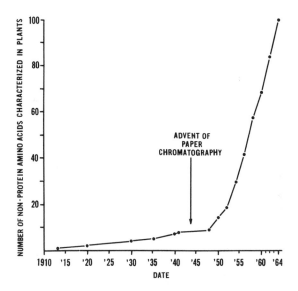

FIG. 6–1. Rate of discovery of new nonprotein amino acids, most of which have been isolated from plants after initially being detected by paper chromatography. [After Fowden, 1962, with permission.]

genes governing their occurrence may have been fixed (in an evolutionary sense) under conditions of rather low selection pressure. Yet, in most examples studied, the compounds are under rather specific genetic control. Hence, the compounds are products of evolution and each has its own evolutionary history. Furthermore, the enzymes (proteins) responsible for the individual factors leading to the production of these compounds have their own evolutionary history, as does the ultimate source of genetic information, DNA. Techniques now being developed will probably allow us to study not only the distributions of these many metabolic by-products (often called secondary compounds), but also their biosynthesis, genetic regulation, and comparative enzymology—including, in favorable situations, the primary structure of the protein constituting the enzyme.

Eventually we will be correlating such data with data on the degree and type of DNA homology among organisms. By DNA homology, at this level, we mean the extent to which the chromosomal DNA spanning a number of functional units presents the same linear sequence of functional units. At a higher level of resolution (intragenically), one can deduce the degree of DNA homology from the primary structures of two homologous but not identical enzymes when the genetic code is completely understood.

Because of the essential unity of life, when fundamental advances are made utilizing one group of organisms, it is highly probable that the new data or the new methods will be applied successfully to other types of living organisms. A good example of this is the recent work on DNA-RNA homology first analyzed in bacteriophages and bacteria and shortly thereafter applied to vertebrates. Thus, even though there are now some technical difficulties in extracting DNA from the well-protected cells of higher plants, it has been the tradition of science to surmount such problems. Similarly, at present the most effective comparative studies of the primary structure of enzyme-like proteins have utilized human hemoglobin, and in principle the type of work currently being done on hemoglobin chemistry can also be done on certain of the seed proteins and some plant enzymes (we will make a brief digression from plants in this connection later on).

DNA-RNA HOMOLOGY

Although in principle the technique for measuring the analysis of DNA-RNA homology is simple enough, it depends upon certain fortuitous properties of DNA in addition to its double-stranded nature, such as its susceptibility to strand dissociation and reassociation under mild conditions. The early studies of DNA homology were based on N^{15}-deuterated DNA from one source, with untreated DNA in the test source. The two were dissociated, mixed, allowed to reassociate, and subjected to density gradient analysis. The amount of the material of intermediate density represented the hybrid. Residual single-stranded DNA can be removed enzymatically by a phosphodiesterase that attacks only this form. Then if half of the DNA were present as the intermediate-density species, this would suggest random duplex formation. This result was obtained when both DNA samples came from the same organism (that is, species, or strain); but when the test DNA came from a different organism, the fraction of duplexed strands of intermediate density decreased. Since duplex formation is based apparently on the extent of DNA resemblance, somewhat analogously to chromosomal synapsis in meiosis, it is obvious that a major technical breakthrough is represented by such methods. Other workers modified the methods by trapping the dissociated DNA in agar particles and extended the work to a comparison of the degree of duplex formation between RNA and single-stranded DNA. Figure 6–2 illustrates the method used, in this instance to analyze the binding of labeled, fragmented (sheared) DNA to immobilized separated strands

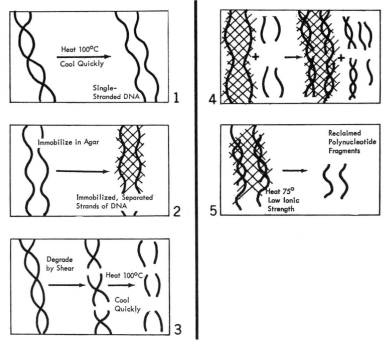

FIG. 6–2. Summary of method used in the analysis of DNA homology of different organisms. [Hoyer, McCarthy, and Bolton, 1964. *Science,* Vol. 144 (May 22, 1964), p. 960.]

of DNA. Uncombined sheared DNA is washed out, and the radioactivity residing in the duplex provides a measurement of the extent of binding of the test DNA— that is, an approximation of the degree of its homology with the standard. Scientists at the Carnegie Institution of Washington have now applied such techniques successfully to compare a number of vertebrates. Much refinement of methodology is needed before systematists can afford to employ the data liberally, but it is especially significant that, using different variations in methodology, one can measure DNA homology either among orders of vertebrates or, as in the early work, at the species or even varietal level among microorganisms.

COMPARATIVE PRIMARY STRUCTURE OF PROTEINS

The first protein to have the linear sequence of its amino acids (primary structure) analyzed successfully was insulin, a comparatively small molecule of about fifty amino acids. Then, a number of other proteins were characterized, and some comparative analyses commonly disclosed minor differences in the amino acid sequences of presumably homologous proteins. A major link between protein chemistry and biochemical genetics was Ingram's disclosure that sickle cell hemoglobin (a single-gene-governed condition) differed from normal hemoglobin in one amino acid (valine replacing glutamic acid) of the beta chain of adult hemoglobin. Following this work, numerous unusual hemoglobin types have been detected, with electrophoretic screening to detect aberrant hemoglobins, and increased accuracy and efficiency in peptide analysis. Most of the hemoglobin types differing in primary structure involve single amino acid substitutions that can be interpreted, according to current understanding of the genetic code, as the result of single nucleotide changes. In vertebrates (lamprey and hagfish excepted), hemoglobin consists of four identical nonprotein units (heme units, which are ferroporphyrins) plus four protein chains, nearly always found as two pairs of two different, although similar, chains. The human adult hemoglobin major fraction (HbA) contains two alpha chains (141 amino acids) and two beta chains (150 amino acids) giving a molecular weight of about 68,000. This is four times the weight of lamprey hemoglobin, which consists of one heme plus one chain. Lamprey hemoglobin is similar in size to myoglobin (the oxygen carrier of muscle tissue), although the amino acid sequence of whale myoglobin is quite different from any hemoglobin chains analyzed so far. Myoglobin is regarded as the prototype of the hemoglobins and it has been suggested that the genetic loci governing the formation of hemoglobin itself may have originated from the myoglobin locus by virtue of unequal crossing over followed by independent evolution.

In most vertebrates a fetal hemoglobin is produced until shortly after birth. This hemoglobin consists of two normal alpha chains, but the beta chains are replaced by two gamma chains. The gamma chain has twenty-three acid differences from the beta chain, plus an amino acid (isoleucine) not present in the alpha or beta chains. Recently, normal adults have been found to contain a second hemoglobin component (HbA$_2$), constituting up to 15 percent. In HbA$_2$ the two normal alpha chains are present, but a pair of delta chains replace the beta chains. The delta chain differs only in ten amino acids from the beta chain. Although hemoglobins of abnormal alpha chain and of abnormal beta chain occur in nearly the same number of variants, the former type never seems to be present, even regionally, in a very large number of individuals. The explanation has been offered that an alpha chain modification must succeed in conferring selective advantage simultaneously to three different types of hemoglobin, all of which doubtlessly have special roles. Therefore, in an evolutionary sense, the alpha chain is relatively conservative.

A mass of circumstantial evidence points to an evolutionary history of the various protein chains of hemoglobin, as visualized in Fig. 6–3.

Not only does the close primary structural resemblance between the beta and the delta chains imply closer evolutionary relationship between these two, but the genetic loci governing these two chains are closely linked. In fact, in the aberrant hemoglobin type, Lepore, there is a single gene known to involve, simultaneously, absence of the beta chain and a modification of the delta chain. This situation may possibly represent an overlapping deletion affecting both genes governing respectively the beta and delta chains.

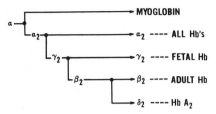

FIG. 6–3. Hypothetical stages in the evolution of protein chains of primate hemoglobin. [After Ingram, 1963.]

Further insight into the possible relationship between the beta chain and the gamma chain of fetal hemoglobin has come from some recent work by a group of investigators at Duke University. They studied intensively the alpha and beta chains of a large number of primates, down to lemurs and a tree shrew. Following presently accepted theories of relationships among the primates, these generalizations can be made with respect to alpha and beta hemoglobin chains:

1. In general as one proceeds from the higher primates downward, the degree of divergence of the alpha and the beta protein chains from those of human HbA increases.
2. The alpha chain appears to be more conservative, but both qualitative and quantitative changes in the two chains are common and diverse.
3. Some regions of the protein chains are particularly conservative (for example, beta tryptic peptide IV and alpha tryptic peptide IX). These regions may have some special role in determining the critical steric properties of the molecule.
4. Not only does isoleucine appear in the beta chain of the primitive primates, but among these organisms the beta chain tends to resemble more closely the human gamma chain, and the differences between the beta chain of humans and that of the lower primates are predominantly at the same places at which human beta and gamma chains differ.

The kinds of data now being obtained on comparative macromolecular chemistry are exciting to scientists interested in evolutionary biology. As indicated earlier, electrophoretic screening of hemoglobins has disclosed many new types of "abnormal" hemoglobins. This technique is being used widely by zoologists and botanists. One system well suited to such studies is the storage proteins of seeds of many plants of the bean family (Leguminosae). A typical electrophoretic pattern is illustrated in Fig. 6–4. Note that a total of at least thirteen components can be detected in this material. Although these techniques are now providing just empirical taxonomic data, they will probably be the vehicle through which protein components will be selected for more complete characterization.

Another method of comparatively studying proteins involves the use of animal hosts to develop antibodies to individual proteins (antigens) extracted from the test organism and injected into the host. Since antibodies by definition interact

FIG. 6–4. Electrophoretic separation of seed proteins of *Phaseolus*.
[Fox, Thurman and Boulter, 1964, with permission of authors and
Phytochemistry.]

with their corresponding antigens (typically to form a precipitate), one can
determine whether or not two species have similar antigens by measuring the
response of the host's antibodies to an extract from the same source (homologous
reaction) and then comparing the degree and nature of the response to an
extract from some other source (heterologous reaction). The homologous
reaction should, theoretically, be greater than the heterologous reaction. The
degree of relationship can thus be inferred from the degree of reaction with
the heterologous protein extract. A technique known as immunoelectrophoresis
makes it possible to separate the individual antigens and therefore introduces
a qualitative basis for the comparison of antigens. Figure 6–5 illustrates the

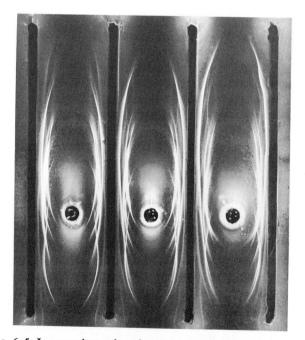

FIG. 6–5. Immunoelectrophoretic patterns in *Baptisia*. Antiserum to
Baptisia nuttalliana is placed into vertical troughs and seed-protein
extracts from three species of *Baptisia* to be tested are placed in
circular cups. Precipitin arcs represent antigen-antibody interactions.
[Lester, Alston and Turner, 1965.]

type of data that may be obtained by immunoelectrophoresis. These serological methods, as they are known, have been applied successfully to a study of the proteins of rye and wheat hybrids, and the antigenic composition of the hybrids is essentially the sum of the antigenic complements of the parents.

SECONDARY COMPOUNDS

Secondary compounds are small molecular-weight compounds not essential to the life of the individual cell but part of the biology of the species as it is adapted to the environment. The compounds all have an evolutionary history, though parallel and convergent evolution may obscure the history of chemistry as well as structure. Among the vascular plants, these compounds number into the thousands, and new molecular types are constantly being discovered. Some of these simple molecules are of widespread occurrence (for example, p-hydroxy benzoic acid); others occur irregularly among widely separate groups (for example, nicotine); and still others are restricted to a few species of one genus (for example, lathyrine; Fig. 6–6).

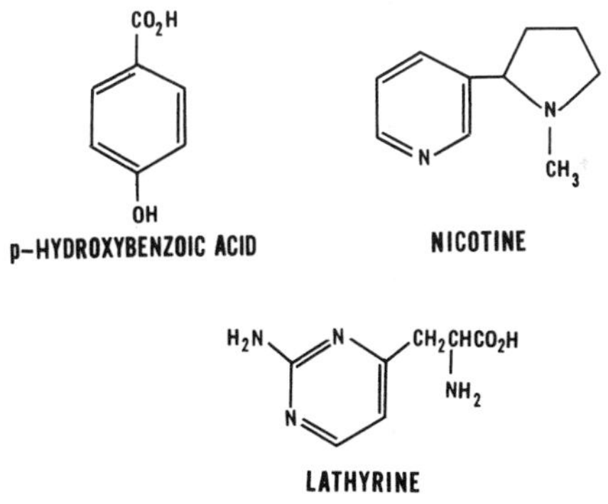

p-HYDROXYBENZOIC ACID   NICOTINE

LATHYRINE

FIG. 6–6. Simple secondary compounds having, individually, quite different ranges of taxonomic distributions.

Although secondary compounds are in general mysterious in their biosynthetic and functional attributes, some generalizations are valid. For example, one major biosynthetic route (the shikimic acid pathway) leading to the aromatic amino acids such as tyrosine, and to lignin precursors such as coniferyl alcohol, has been usurped by selection pressure, and now among the lignin-producing plants it also provides important precursors for the flower pigments (anthocyanins) (Fig. 6–7). In addition to the well-known flower pigments, there are hundreds of related compounds (flavonoids), each with but slight modifications of a basic type, formed by this same pathway.

A second major pathway involves the condensation of two-carbon units formed in the course of the well-known respiratory pathway. This acetoacetyl condensation gives rise to the fatty acids (basic metabolites), but in addition it probably leads to the formation of the bizarre acetylenic compounds found in various plants. Also, acetate condensation may provide a part of some secondary compounds (for example, in the red flower pigment in Fig. 6–7, it provides the six-membered ring at left).

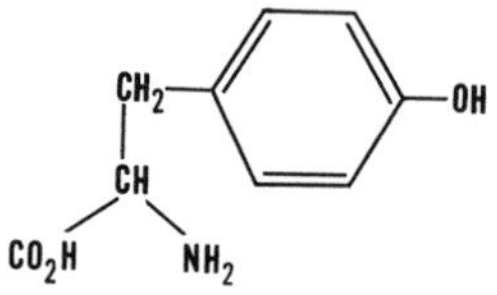

TYROSINE 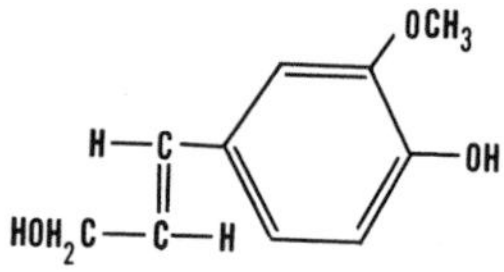   CONIFERYL ALCOHOL

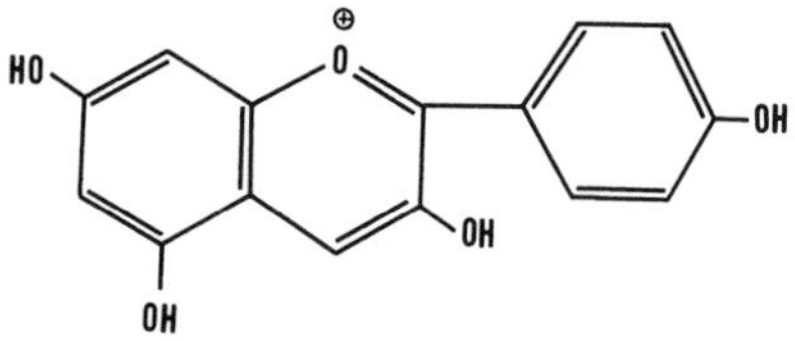

PELARGONIDIN
(Red Flower Pigment)

FIG. 6–7. Compounds of diverse nature having a common early biosynthetic history by way of the shikimic acid pathway.

A third major pathway (the mevalonic acid pathway) leads to "isoprenoid" compounds such as the phytyl group of chlorophyl, the carotenoids, plastoquinones, steroids, and others. This pathway has been responsible for the origin of a vast number of volatile secondary compounds, the terpenes, which produce most of the odoriferous plant products.

All three of the above pathways may combine to produce a single compound such as rotenone shown in Fig. 6–8. It might be expected that compounds of such complexity would have more limited distributions, and indeed rotenones are

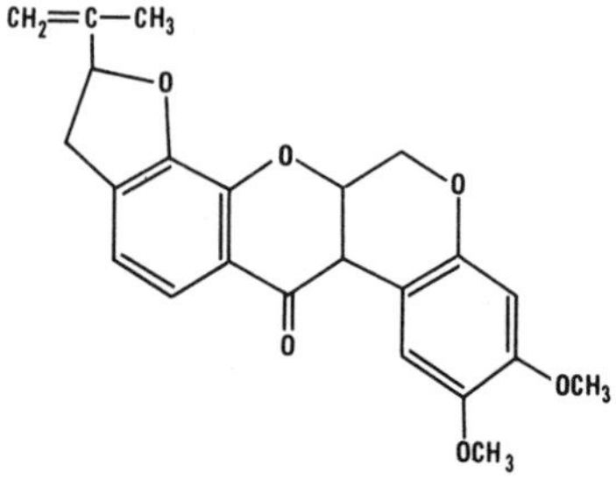

ROTENONE

FIG. 6–8. Rotenone, a product of three separate major biosynthetic systems.

limited to a relatively few genera of one subfamily of the Leguminosae. This tendency was recognized much earlier by pharmocologists and chemists and expressed as the "percentage of frequency rule" (that is, the taxonomic distribution of a secondary compound is inversely proportional to its biological complexity—not necessarily its molecular weight). Although the correlating of the taxonomic distributions of these small-molecular-weight substances is not so elegant as the macromolecular studies described earlier, there occur some remarkable examples of taxonomic correlations, some interesting examples leading to phylogenetic deductions, and some peculiar situations that are provocative and without explanation. Only a few examples can be given here.

Alkaloids, which are somewhat arbitrarily defined as nitrogen-containing substances usually having physiological activity in animals, are of heterogeneous origin. Their biosynthesis may be regarded as derived from one or more of the protein amino acids. Hegnauer has classified alkaloids into "families" on the basis of their presumptive origins from a specific amino acid—a convenient but arbitrary classification since the biosyntheses of most of the several thousand alkaloids are obscure. However, there is no doubt that natural groups of alkaloids exist, and this fact is often supported by their taxonomic distributions. The isoquinoline alkaloids, for example, appear to form a natural, quite numerous group, apparently derived from the tyrosine pathway. A series of forms of isoquinoline alkaloids have been described, but they can be placed conveniently into "natural" series (Fig. 6–9). Furthermore, with few exceptions, these alkaloids are found in a group of families long considered by many taxonomists to represent a natural group comprising the order Ranales. In this instance the overall taxonomic-chemical correlations are loose, and as yet no deep phylogenetic insight is provided by the chemical data. Other types of alkaloids (for example, the necine types of *Senecio*) may be found only in a single genus and could be looked upon as generic key characters.

One of the most interesting examples of a group of compounds whose distribution appears to be of major phylogenetic significance involves the betacyanins (beet pigments formerly erroneously called "nitrogenous anthocyanins"). These compounds were recently characterized by Dreiding and co-workers at Zurich. The betacyanins contain nitrogen in both an indole and a pyridine ring, and it is clear from their structure (Fig. 6–10) that they are chemically unrelated to the anthocyanins. The betacyanin pigments occur in approximately ten families, most of which have been placed by taxonomists in the order Centrospermae. Included are such familiar plants as beets and cacti. The families that produce betacyanins apparently do not produce anthocyanins, so these pigments are mutually exclusive. Since the only property that the two types of compounds share is color (their absorption maxima are both close to 545 millimicrons), it is tempting to deduce that the major role of the compounds in the plant involves color.

Not all of the plants that produce betacyanins have been placed by all tax-

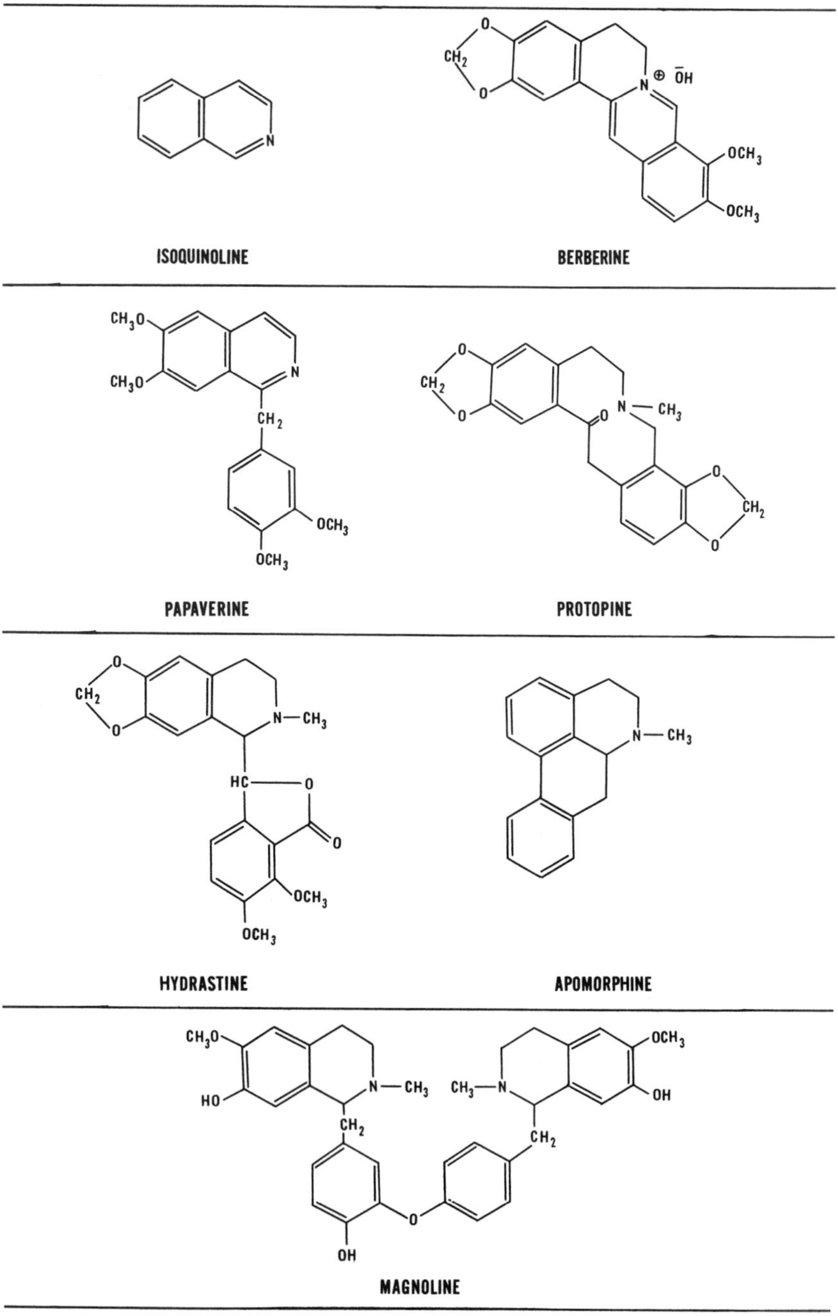

ISOQUINOLINE

BERBERINE

PAPAVERINE

PROTOPINE

HYDRASTINE

APOMORPHINE

MAGNOLINE

FIG. 6–9. Alkaloids of the isoquinoline type, presumed to be biosynthetically related. Their taxonomic distributions tend to reinforce the presumptive biosynthetic homogeneity.

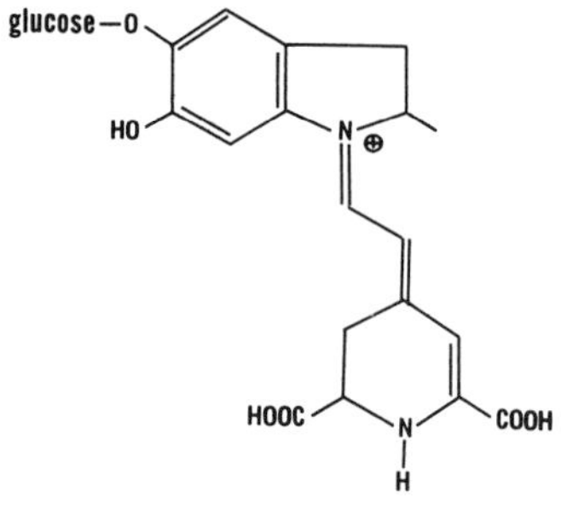

BETANIN

FIG. 6–10. Betanin, red beet pigment formerly thought to be an anthocyanin. This pigment is not known to occur together with anthocyanin in a plant.

onomists in the Centrospermae. The most striking example is the family Didieraceae, spiny xerophytic trees found only in Madagascar. Its taxonomic position has been disputed, but at least one worker in the nineteenth century related this family to the Centrospermae. Also, the genus *Stegnosperma*, which was recently removed from the Centrospermae by a well-known taxonomist, has been shown by Mabry and co-workers to produce betacyanins. While chemical information is undoubtedly of major taxonomic importance, chemical data such as these may also raise many serious problems concerning the equitable evaluation of the chemistry in the context of a lot of morphological data. The problem of weighting data in taxonomy is especially disturbing. For example, is *Stegnosperma* in a natural taxonomic position outside the Centrospermae if it produces betacyanins? If we knew that betacyanins arose only once in the course of evolution, it would facilitate our decision. Suppose we concluded on chemical and biological grounds that it was probably unlikely that betacyanins evolved independently more than once. Could we use this knowledge to discard one or several major morphological differences as relatively insignificant at the ordinal level? Even if a taxonomist were to evade the immediate challenge to use such data on the grounds of academic pragmatism, the betacyanins will not go away. Perhaps one solution will be to equate all taxonomic characters, including chemical, to a unit value and employ the principles of numerical taxonomy as described by Sokal and others. Numerical taxonomy is certainly abstract and quantitative enough to give taxonomy the aura of an exact science (this will come as somewhat of a surprise to those dedicated taxonomists who think taxonomy an art!).

An example of a rather mysterious chemical correlation is provided by the monotypic genus *Casuarina*, a tree native to Australia and Malaya. This tree is the only flowering plant (angiosperm) known to produce compounds called biflavonyls, although these compounds are found in many conifers, in ginkgo, and in cycads. Furthermore, the taxonomic position of *Casuarina* has long been debated. Some taxonomists have considered it to be the most primitive angiosperm, deriving it from an *Ephedra*-like ancestor; others have looked upon it as a highly specialized member of the order Hamamelidales, which contains the common sycamore tree. Finally, in its lignin chemistry, *Casuarina* has an extremely low relative proportion of syringyl subunits, atypical of most angiosperms but similar to certain conifers such as *Podocarpus*, also of Australia. It is difficult for the taxonomist to ignore these interesting chemical features of *Casuarina* in considering the natural affinities of the plant, yet it is far from clear that such chemical parallelisms constitute valid phylogenetic links.

SECONDARY COMPOUNDS AS VALID TAXONOMIC MARKERS

In formal genetic studies, secondary compounds such as mint oils, flower pigments, and the like have usually been considered genetically regulated. Some of the classic studies on the structural gene and gene expressivity in corn have utilized anthocyanin markers. Even so, it is also true that a large number of environmental factors tend to influence quantitatively the formation of anthocyanins (although qualitative effects are rarely encountered). Therefore, taxonomists have to be extremely cautious in accepting a chemical character as valid taxonomically until it has been proven reliable, although but a casual reflection upon anthocyanin pigmentation of species in nature will serve as a reminder that the flower colors of violets, paintbrushes, orchids, bluebells, and others are often as dependable as are their details of form and structure. When the more numerous unseen relatives of flower pigments (the other flavonoids) are considered, it is not possible merely to assume that such compounds are consistent in their presence or absence. They may appear only at certain developmental stages, or only in certain ecological situations. Many alkaloids tend to be present in much higher quantity in very young plants, and studies of some cyanide-producing plants have shown them to be susceptible to climatic fluctuations, so that in certain years they may contain little of the cyanogenetic substance. Such a quantitative variation may be expected in compounds that do not have an important role in the life of the individual plant. Flavors and odors, of course, emanate from a specific group of secondary compounds, and these compounds, though invisible, are generally quite reliable—hence, sassafras tea is distinctive in its odor and taste.

For systematic purposes, most broad generalizations about secondary compounds are inadequate because of numerous exceptions, so each investigator must establish to his own complete satisfaction the validity of the chemical data with which he might be concerned. Naturally, the reliability of data is likely to appear to be low when techniques for obtaining data are crude; and variation that seems excessive in a few individuals may often have meaningful patterns if many individuals or appropriate growth stages or many different populations are analyzed. McClure completed recently one of the most thorough studies of the reliability of a number of flavonoids as taxonomic aids, using one of the smallest flowering plants, *Spirodela*. This aquatic plant, only a few millimeters long, can be grown on a completely defined medium under sterile conditions. McClure varied the conditions of growth in many ways, utilizing a total of fifty-eight different treatments including some media to which growth factors like auxin or gibberellic acid had been added. In almost every instance the pattern of flavonoid chemistry was practically unchanged. Although it is difficult to explain, many different flavonoids were present in this simple plant and the formation of the flavonoids was controlled so completely by intrinsic factors that the compounds were nearly immune to ecological factors.

A number of taxonomists have reported on the use of paper chromatographic methods to expose the patterns of secondary compounds (mostly phenolic compounds) that typify the flowers or leaves of particular species. Often, few of these compounds are present, but in other instances many different compounds occur, and the complex two-dimensional chromatographic patterns alone allow immediate recognition of the species. The seeming vagaries of flavonoid chemistry are such that it is not possible to predict that morphological attributes will serve as indicators of what to expect in the chromatographic patterns. For example, the simple duckweeds (*Spirodela,* discussed above, is in this group) are sometimes unidentifiable on morphological grounds, yet the different species are extremely distinctive in their flavonoid chemistry. In contrast, *Psoralea* (in the bean family), a genus containing a number of species individually quite distinctive morphologically, seems to have a recurrent pattern of flavonoid chemistry that is nearly genus specific. Yet prominent features of flavonoid chemistry in both duckweeds and *Psoralea* are a relatively rare group of compounds called glycoflavones.

Most taxonomic studies of flavonoids have illustrated the utility of flavonoids as taxonomic markers within a group. But these compounds are quite widespread; and like nicotine, discussed earlier, a flavonoid may appear again and again among widely separated plant groups. Many systematists have stressed that new types of data from a new approach may be given more credence than is justified, merely because of the novelty of the data or their somewhat esoteric nature. Thus, chemical data should be used cautiously as the sole basis for phylogenetic speculations.

CHEMICAL SYSTEMATIC STUDIES OF NATURAL HYBRIDIZATION

The use of biochemical markers in the study of Mendelian genetics goes back many years. Some of these investigations used interspecific crosses. But until the late 1950s, there was little interest in the simultaneous use of a number of different chemical markers to analyze interspecific hybridization in nature. In one of the first of these early studies, Mirov used the oil characters of two species of pines. He found that species-specific chemical components of the pine oil appeared together in the putative hybrids. Australian workers using the oil characters of *Eucalyptus* noted the same additive pattern and also established that certain minor components of the *Eucalyptus* oils were increased among the hybrids. Using *Baptisia,* we also discovered that the species-specific flavonoids of the parents were present together in the interspecific hybrids. All this early work, then, disclosed an important principle that distinguishes the chemistry of hybrids from the morphology of hybrids. In general, hybrids are morphologically intermediate between the parents, and the rule tends to hold even for individual characters such as petiole length, pubescence, leaf shape, and others. In contrast, in their secondary chemistry, hybrids tend to contain a summation of species-specific compounds, although theoretically numerous exceptions might be expected.

A remarkable example of biochemical supplementation or summation in hybrids is seen in some recent work on fern hybrids by Smith and Levin.

The fern *Asplenium* is known to be involved in rather complex interspecific hybridization. Among this complex, several hybrid species have been recognized. Cytological analyses have served to substantiate in part the hypothetical derivation of some of these hybrid groups. The original, parental complex is thought to include three taxa: *A. montanum* (with a chromosome number of $2n=72$; genotype$=$MM); *A. platyneuron* ($2n=72$; genotype$=$PP); and *A. rhizophyllum* ($2n=72$; genotype$=$RR). Two taxa of hybrid origin are *A.* x *kentuckiense,* a triploid of composition MPR, and *A.* x *gravesii,* a tetraploid of composition MMPR. Each of these hybrids has then a set of genes from three different species. Upon chromatographic analysis of the three parental species, each was found to have compounds lacking in the other two species. Furthermore, the two hybrids contained essentially a complete set of the compounds from all three species (Fig. 6–11). This is the first example of the use of chemical markers

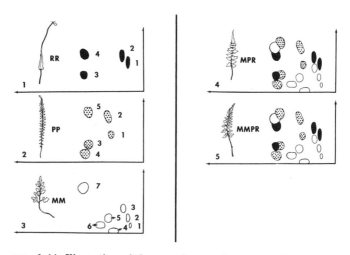

FIG. 6–11. Illustration of the use of paper chromatography to confirm theoretical assumptions as to the origins of certain *Asplenium* taxa. 1. *Asplenium rhizophyllum.* 2. *A. platyneuron.* 3. *A. montanum.* 4. *A.* x *kentuckiense.* 5. *A.* x *gravesii.* [Smith and Levin, 1963.]

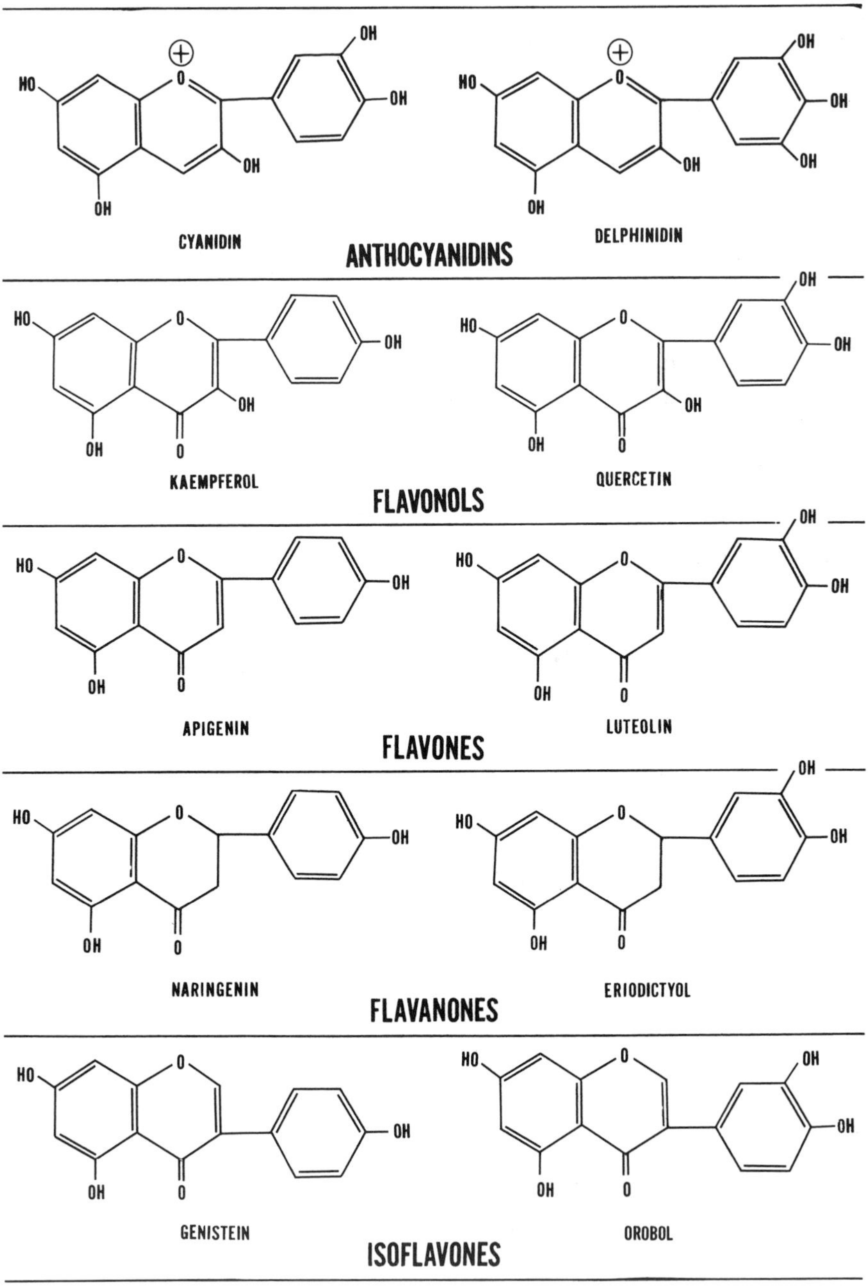

FIG. 6–12. Some examples of flavonoid aglycone types characterized in *Baptisia* species.

to establish the simultaneous presence of three genomes in a single individual. For several years we and our associates at The University of Texas have intensively investigated the genus *Baptisia*. Although comparative chemical studies of the uncommon lupinine-type alkaloids in *Baptisia* are also in progress, the most intensive study has been on the flavonoids of this genus. At least two basic ring structures of each of five different subtypes of flavonoids have been identified in *Baptisia,* and many other flavonoids remain to be characterized (Fig. 6–12). Thus, a rather large number of secondary compounds is available. All of the species (about twenty) of *Baptisia* are restricted to the central and eastern United States; the largest number occur in the Southeast. The species are in most instances quite distinct, and they are readily identified morphologically. In spite of the distinctive nature of the species, hybridization is common in *Baptisia*. At least fourteen different natural hybrid combinations occur, and in one field four different species and all six of the possible interspecific hybrid types have been detected by use of a combination of morphological and chemical data. Not all *Baptisia* hybrids can be validated purely on chemical grounds—at least not readily. However, some species differ in a large number of flavonoids, and the hybrid, which has nearly a full complement of compounds of each parental species, is quite distinctive (Fig. 6–13). The same strong general tendency toward cumulative occurrence of species-specific compounds in the hybrid is encountered in *Baptisia* with some general tendency also toward a quantitative increase in the minor components and a decrease in the amounts of some major components. In certain situations, compounds are consistently present in leaves of hybrids, although they are either absent or restricted to flowers in both parental species. This especially interesting phenomenon has been attributed to a breakdown in certain regulatory processes governing the localization of the distribution of the compound, as in flower pigmentation.

In addition to establishing the probable origin of a putative hybrid, the chemical markers have been utilized in population analysis of "hybrid swarms." For example, in a hybridizing population one would like to know, if possible, how long hybridization has been occurring, the incidence of hybridization, whether hybrids are sterile or partially sterile, the nature and extent of backcrossing, the possible selective advantage of the hybrid in an intermediate habitat, the extent to which groups of associated characters are passed collectively to progeny of hybrids, and many other things. These questions are relevant to population dynamics and, in a genetic context, to population genetics. Reliable genetic markers are needed if this type of analysis is to be successful. In *Baptisia* we do not yet have a group of morphological features that serve as unit characters since the hybrid is more or less intermediate for each character, and many morphological traits in the genus seem to be influenced by multiple genetic factors. Therefore, the morphology of the putative hybrid can be expressed most accurately in a cumulative hybrid index. For example, if species A has no stipules and species B has large stipules, a plant without stipules would be scored as 0; a plant with typical stipules would be scored 2. Intermediacy for

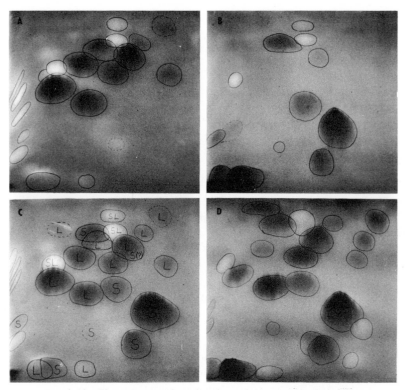

FIG. 6–13. Chromatographic validation of interspecific hybridization of *Baptisia sphaerocarpa* and *B. leucantha*. Two-dimensional chromatograms: (A) of leaf extract of *B. leucantha;* (B) of *B. sphaerocarpa;* (C) of an artificial mixture of the same extracts of the two species; (D) of a natural hybrid of the two species. Hybrids always contain four compounds normally found only in the flowers of *B. sphaerocarpa.* [Alston and Hempel, 1964.]

the character would be scored 1. Some problems of the morphological hybrid index as applied to *Baptisia* are illustrated in Fig. 6–14 which shows hybrids involving the species *B. perfoliata.* In contrast, chemical markers in general can be scored on a presence or absence basis, with the hybrid having approximately the summation of the species-specific compounds (that is, compounds present in only one of the parental species). In hybrid swarms involving *Baptisia* species, when morphological and chemical evidence have been compared, chemical evidence has favored the inference of a simpler populational structure— that is, with relatively few hybrids and very few "backcross" types. Since the morphological data have implied a more complex pattern of hybridization, we are interested in knowing which types of data provide the more accurate picture. Only by producing a number of synthetic hybrids can one establish the

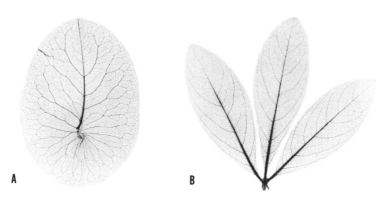

A   B

FIG. 6–14. This series illustrates the morphological variation that may occur at successive internodes of a single shoot of a natural hybrid of *Baptisia perfoliata* x *B. lanceolata*. (A) typical leaf of *B. perfoliata;* (B) typical leaf of *B. lanceolata;* (C–H), at right, sequential series of leaves from a shoot of hybrid. Note, stipules always occur in hybrids involving *B. perfoliata,* although neither parent may be stipulate. The extreme forms of the leaves of the hybrid appear to be similar to hypothetical "backcross" types in either direction. [Clearings of leaves prepared by Mr. Eli Hemenway, University of Texas.]

actual range of variation in the morphology or the chemistry of the F_1 hybrid and its backcrosses. Among the synthetic hybrids of *B. leucophaea* x *B. sphaerocarpa* produced so far, there is considerable variation in the chemical patterns, although all plants can be recognized as hybrids. The plants are not yet old enough to be analyzed morphologically.

When one group of natural "hybrids" was analyzed independently by morphological and chemical criteria, it was concluded that the two lines of evidence agreed in the interpretation of the overall composition of the population, but significantly they disagreed in individual instances. Figure 6–15 illustrates the morphological hybrid index values that were established arbitrarily on the basis of chemical data for three groups of plants (F_1 hybrids plus both backcross types). Although the two different "backcross" groups do not overlap in their morphological hybrid indices, the range of index values of putative F_1 hybrids is very great. Since both types of data cannot be "wrong," and we cannot change the facts, one or another type of data is superior in this particular application. Possibly the degree of variation in both the chemistry and morphology of F_1 hybrids is greater than previously suspected.

As more chemical data are accumulated, and one becomes more familiar with the chromatographic patterns of *Baptisia* leaf and flower extracts, it is possible to envision certain subgeneric patterns based on recurrent associations of flavonoids most prominent by the methods used. In *Baptisia,* three such subgeneric patterns may be recognized, each of which is repeated in part in several

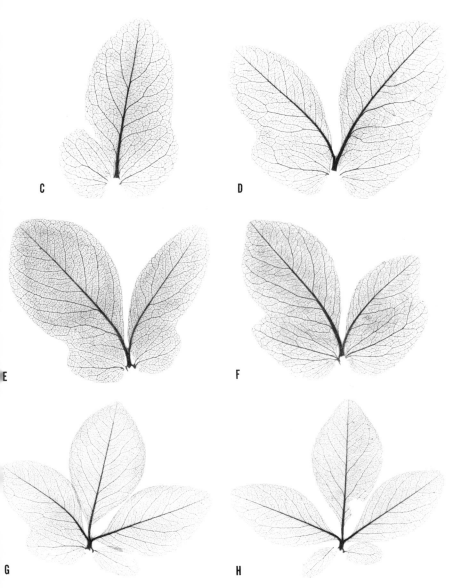

C

D

E

F

G

H

species. In one group of species *(B. leucophaea)* flavone monoglycosides such as apigenin and luteolin 7-monoglycosides are most prominent. In another group *(B. sphaerocarpa)* flavone diglucosides dominate the pattern. In a third group of species *(B. leucantha)* flavonols apparently replace the flavones. These compounds are illustrated in Fig. 6–14. It would be easy, and indeed it is tempting, to group the *Baptisia* species on the basis of their chemical affinities and to develop even a feeling of belief, since scientists are only human, that this evidence points out phylogenetic relationships. The compounds of Fig. 6–14 are exceed-

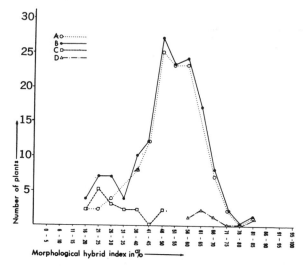

FIG. 6–15. In this diagram, curve A is based on a group of plants designated as F, hybrids of *Baptisia leucantha* and *B. sphaerocarpa;* C is based on a group designated as backcross types to *B. sphaerocarpa;* D is based on a group designated as backcross types to *B. leucantha.* These groups were all arbitrarily established by analysis of chromatographic data on the basis of their flavonoid chemistry. Curve B merely plots all three groups together as a reference. The important point to note is that all plants were analyzed independently and given a "hybrid-index" value. In general, the two types of data are in accord but some of the so-called "F hybrids" have extremely low or extremely high morphological hybrid-index values. [McHale and Alston, 1964.]

ingly common flavonoids, however, and they represent only the most conspicuous elements of the complex secondary chemistry of *Baptisia.* Some of the chemically very interesting isoflavones do not even appear on the chromatograms. Therefore, it is imperative that one show discretion in the interpretation of the evolutionary significance of a small number of rather common flavonoids.

The above account has been devoted to a comprehensive but superficial summary of a variety of approaches to a field that seems to have exciting possibilities for the future. We hope that our appraisal of this field has combined objectivity with tempered optimism.

REFERENCES

ALSTON, R. E., T. J. MABRY, AND B. L. TURNER. "Perspectives in Chemotaxonomy." *Science,* Vol. 142 (1963), pp. 545–552.

————, AND B. L. TURNER. *Biochemical Systematics*. Englewood Cliffs, N.J.: Prentice-Hall, Inc., 1963.

HEGNAUER, R. *Chemotaxonomie der Pflanzen*. Vols. 1–3. Basel: Birkhäuser Verlag, 1962–65.

HOYER, B. H., B. J. MCCARTHY, AND E. T. BOLTON. "A Molecular Approach in the Systematics of Higher Organisms." *Science*, Vol. 144 (1964), pp. 959–967.

INGRAM, V. M. *The Hemoglobins in Genetics and Evolution*. New York: Columbia University Press, 1963.

LANNI, F. "Viruses and Molecular Taxonomy." In *Plant Virology*. Gainesville: University of Florida Press, 1964. 527 pp.

LEONE, C. A., ed. *Taxonomic Biochemistry and Serology*. New York: The Ronald Press Co., 1964.

MABRY, T. J. "The Betacyanins and Betaxanthins." In *A Symposium on Comparative Phytochemistry*, ed. T. Swain. New York: Academic Press, Inc. (in press).

MARGOLIASH, E. "The Amino Acid Sequence of Cytochrome *c* in Relation to Its Function and Evolution." *Canadian Journal of Botany*, Vol. 42 (1964), pp. 745–753.

SMITH, D. M., AND D. A. LEVIN. "A Chromatographic Study of Reticulate Evolution in the Appalachian *Asplenium* Complex." *American Journal of Botany*, Vol. 50 (1963), pp. 952–958.

SWAIN, T., ED. *Chemical Plant Taxonomy*. New York: Academic Press, Inc., 1963.

ZUCKERKANDL, E. "The Evolution of Hemoglobin." *Scientific American*, Vol. 212 (1965), pp. 110–118.

SOME RECENT DEVELOPMENTS IN OUR UNDERSTANDING OF PTERIDOPHYTE AND EARLY GYMNOSPERM EVOLUTION

7

Henry N. Andrews*

Botany Department
University of Connecticut

Several recent discoveries of remarkable fossil plants have greatly advanced our knowledge of the pteridophytes and early gymnosperms. In some ways the old problems have been shown to be more complex than we formerly suspected; the kinds of pteridophytic plants have increased to a point where one must force the newly discovered ones into taxonomic categories where they clearly stand out as misfits, or one may set up many new categories and incite the criticism of botanists who have failed to recognize how complex the picture is becoming. In any event no one can deny that distinctly new and exciting plants are coming to light, and it is safe to predict that many more will become known as the search continues.

I have not intended in this article to suggest that we are close to solving all of the great problems of early vascular plant evolution. There will be no attempt here to present a comprehensive review; it seems more appropriate and informative to consider in some detail a few of the more important discoveries that are influencing our understanding and theories of vascular plant evolution. The discoveries that I wish to consider may be grouped under three subject areas:

1. Evidence pertaining to the oldest clearly recognizable vascular land plants.
2. Certain evolutionary patterns in pteridophytic plants in the Devonian and Carboniferous periods.
3. The origin of the seed and early evolution of seed plants.

* I wish to express my gratitude for grants-in-aid that I have received from the National Science Foundation and the John Simon Guggenheim Memorial Foundation. Although the grants were not made for the preparation of this article, they have helped me indirectly in many ways.

THE EARLIEST VASCULAR PLANTS

During the past half century, paleobotanists have grasped eagerly at any evidence bearing on the origin and early evolution of vascular plants. Our knowledge of them from horizons below the Devonian is still extremely scanty and largely controversial. Since it has been established that plant life existed some 1.7 billion years ago, vascular plants probably came into existence much earlier than the Devonian, but the record is far from satisfactory. Two problems in particular must be kept in mind in interpreting Lower Devonian and presumed pre-Devonian plant remains: the all too imperfect preservation, and the difficulty in many instances of making exact stratigraphic determinations.

The oldest generally accepted record for vascular plants is that of the "Baragwanathia flora" of Australia, described as Silurian in age. Three distinct plants are included in the flora: *Baragwanathia* (probably a lycopod), and *Yarravia* and *Hedeia* of less certain relationships. These fossils have been mentioned in the literature many times and need not be described here. It is important to note that they represent considerable diversity in the morphology of their spore-bearing parts, and this diversity may indicate a significant vascular plant ancestry of which we know almost nothing. The Silurian age of these plants was determined primarily by associated graptolites, and Jaeger (1962) notes that he cannot distinguish the Australian graptolites from Lower Devonian species found in Germany. This evidence, combined with the complexity and diversity of the three Australian genera as compared with other early vascular plants, suggests that they may well be of Devonian rather than Silurian age.*

Quite a few tantalizing reports of plant fragments have been found in pre-Devonian rocks. Spores have been reported from horizons as old as the Cambrian, and some of them may represent vascular plants. A short time ago Dr. William Evitt kindly allowed me to illustrate a tracheidal fragment (Andrews, 1961, p. 48) from the Silurian that suggests a fairly advanced type of vascular plant. But evidence of this sort falls short of being wholly convincing; at best it may strongly suggest that vascular plants did exist, but it tells us very little else about them.

A few significant macrofossil fragments found recently are somewhat more satisfying:

In 1962 Roselt described some fossil remains from the Upper Silurian (Ludlovian) of Saxony that are of more than passing interest. Given the name *Saxonia microphylla*, they consist of dichotomizing shoots (Fig. 7–1A,B) bearing appendages that appear to be densely arranged microphylls. The portions of the shoot system preserved are about .7 cm in diameter. The appendages are 2 to 3 mm long, .5 mm broad, and contain a dark longitudinal line that may

---

* I am indebted to Dr. H. P. Banks for calling my attention to this new evidence concerning the Australian fossils.

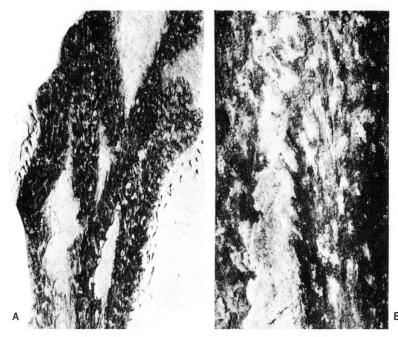

FIG. 7–1A, B. *Saxonia microphylla*. An impression fossil that appears to consist of dichotomizing shoots bearing numerous small leaves. The shoots are about .7 cm in diameter; a portion of one is shown enlarged in (B). From the Upper Silurian of Saxony. [From Roselt, 1962.]

represent a vascular strand; no cellular structure is preserved. These may be shoot fragments of lycopodiaceous affinities; but reproductive organs and positive evidence of vascular tissue are lacking, and Roselt is careful to point out that it is not proven that they are plants.

Another problematical little fragment was reported by Obrhel (1959) that came from Ordovician rocks in central Bohemia. It was actually found back in 1926, rediscovered by Obrhel in the Prague National Museum, and given the name *Boiophyton progense*. It is an unbranched fragment 38 mm long and 1.5 to 2 mm broad with closely appressed, more or less needle-like leaves that are .5 mm thick and not more than 4 mm long.

Saxonia and *Boiophyton* may be vascular plants, but this is by no means certain. However, more convincing evidence of vascular plants in the Silurian comes from another report by Obrhel (1962) describing specimens of *Cooksonia* from Bohemia (Fig. 7–2A,B). This is a genus of delicately dichotomizing leafless shoots that was founded by W. H. Lang in 1937 on specimens from a Downtonian (basal Devonian or late Silurian?) horizon in England; the terminal sporangia are spherical or slightly broader than long. Obrhel's specimens are

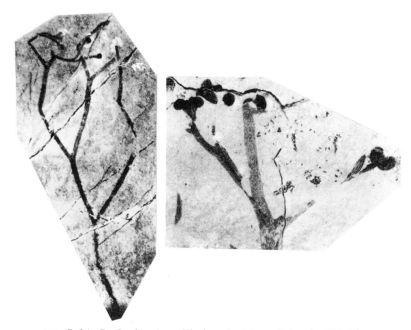

FIG. 7–2A, B. *Cooksonia*, a Silurian plant from Bohemia. (B) The small dichotomizing shoot system displays a dark central line that probably represents vascular tissue; the terminal sporangia are about 1 mm in diameter. [From Obrhel in *Geologie*, 1962.]

only a few centimeters long; they display the terminal sporangia as well as a dark slender strand in the shoots that very likely represents vascular tissue.

The last fossil that I wish to consider in this section comes from the more recent base of the Upper Carboniferous. It may represent a carry-over of the more primitive vascular plants of the early Devonian, or it may be only the fertile portion of a much larger plant; it thus shows the kind of problem one is confronted with in interpreting these early pteridophytic fossils. The plant in question is *Paulophyton jongmansi* (Fig. 7–3), described by the great German paleobotanist Richard Kraüsel, from the Namurian of the Ruhr region. The largest preserved part of the plant is an axis 3 cm broad; branches diverge from the axis in a more or less dichotomous fashion but, as may be noted in the restoration drawing, the dichotomies are often unequal—a mixture of pinnate, palmate, and dichotomous branching. The ultimate divisions usually consist of an equal fork, each subdivision terminating in a swollen tip presumed to have been a sporangium (although spores have not been found in the sporangia). The sporangia are slightly elongate and just a trifle under 3 mm in their greatest diameter.

In his description of these fossils, Kraüsel (1957) notes that if only the sporangia were found (including the ultimate branchlets on which they were

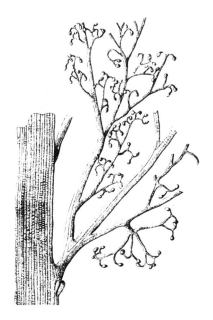

FIG. 7–3. *Paulophyton jongmansi,* a presumed psilophyte from the Upper Carboniferous of the Ruhr region; however, the main axis shown here (3 cm broad) is exceptionally large for a psilophyte. [From Kräusel, 1957. From *Mededel. Geol. Stichting,* Vol. 11.]

borne), and if the fossil came from the Lower Devonian, it would be referred to the genus *Dawsonites,* which may represent the fertile parts of *Psilophyton.* *Psilophyton* is a problematical fossil from the Gaspé first described by the Canadian naturalist J. W. Dawson in 1859. It was probably a plant a foot or two high, of dichotomous habit with upright shoots that bore small spinelike appendages (leaves), creeping rhizomes that may or may not have had such appendages, and possibly small pear-shaped sporangia at the tips of some of the branchlets, although they have not been found in organic connection.

In any event, if the branchlets of *Paulophyton jongmansi* (exclusive of the 3 cm axis) were found in a Lower Devonian horizon, it would be regarded as a "primitive psilophyte," but its presence in the basal part of the Lower Carboniferous sheds some doubt on this relationship. It may be argued quite reasonably that psilophytes lived on into the Carboniferous, but a specimen with an axis 3 cm broad suggests that this may be simply a part of the frond of a much larger plant.

SOME EVOLUTIONARY PATTERNS IN DEVONIAN AND CARBONIFEROUS PTERIDOPHYTIC PLANTS

If the record of the ultimate origins of vascular plants is still obscure, some compensation is afforded by the more generous offerings of the mid-Devonian and later times. As our knowledge of these plants develops, it reveals an increasingly diverse assemblage. Even many of the better-known fossils are difficult to classify. Some may be early representatives of the articulates, while others are starting points for the ferns, but more often their affinities are not clear cut. I have chosen two plants from the Middle Devonian as representative of the highly significant information that the fossil record can give us. Both of them came from a quarry in eastern Belgium where Professor Suzanne Leclercq of the University of Liège has collected a remarkable flora; when it is completely studied it will constitute one of the most informative chapters in our knowledge of the plants of past ages.

Pseudosporochnus nodosus (Leclercq and Banks, 1962) is known from an abundant assemblage of fossil remains that reveal many of the important aspects of the plant. It was probably a small tree with a main trunk up to 8 cm in diameter; the maximum length that this attained is not known, but the plant is thought to have been several feet tall. The main stem bore a crown of primary branches, and these in turn divided two or three times to produce secondary or tertiary branches as shown in the restoration (Fig. 7–4). A terminal portion of the plant is shown at a higher magnification in Fig. 7–5. The ultimate divisions, referred to as fronds, may be wholly sterile or a mixture of sterile and fertile "pinnae"; in the latter case the ultimate branchlets of a pinna are terminated by a pair of sporangia.

Fragments of the first-, second-, and third-order branches have been found partially petrified. For the most part only the stele is preserved; although much crushed, it was evidently a lobed, radially symmetrical structure composed of occasionally anastomosing primary wood segments (Fig. 7–6). Small ovoid vascular strands, slightly elongate in a tangential plane, were given off from the peripheral points of the stele, and these pass into the base of the morphological unit that is referred to as a *frond*. The distinctive structure of the traces, as compared with the stelar anatomy, is important in delimiting the fronds as such.

The cortical tissues of *Pseudosporochnus nodosus* possess abundant and distinctive small patches of sclerotic cells; these were relied on in associating the various parts and assembling them as shown in the restoration.

One may next ask "What is *Pseudosporochnus?* How should it be classified?" As may be noted in their title, the authors place the plant in the Cladoxylales. This is a fossil group of some seven genera of plants known for the most part from complex and diverse stelar types. In only one other species is the general morphology of the plant known; it therefore seems to me that there is inadequate evidence to accept it as a natural order of plants. The importance of *P. nodosus* can hardly be overestimated, but I would hazard the prediction that if the other genera that have been assigned to the Cladoxylales eventually become as well known, some of them may turn out to be very different plants.

It is easier to criticize than it is to come forth with a better classification of *Pseudosporochnus*. Quite clearly the plant is far advanced from the psilophytes.

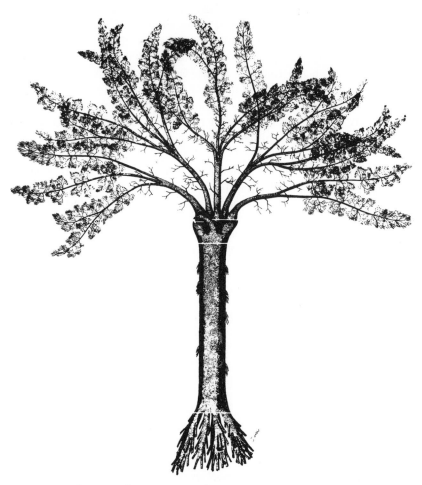

FIG. 7–4. *Pseudosporochnus nodosus,* restoration of the entire plant. [From Leclercq and Banks, 1962.]

even though one defines the latter group in the broadest sense. It is unique in the crownlike development of the primary branches, and there is a tendency for the second-order branches to be similarly organized. It is not difficult to visualize the dichotomously branching "pinnae" as structures that might have become webbed to produce a lamina; however, it does stretch the limits of the ferns (Filicales and Marattiales) to consider it as such. It seems to me that the importance of *Pseudosporochnus* lies in the fact that we have an exceptionally clear understanding of the plant as a whole; it is unique in several aspects and adds greatly to our knowledge of primitive pteridophytes, and it is reasonable to regard it as a member of the broad stream of evolution that led from the

FIG. 7–5. *Pseudosporochnus nodosus.* A terminal branch bearing
sterile and fertile fronds. This is in some ways intermediate between
the simple land plants (psilophytes) of the early Devonian and the
ferns of the late Devonian and Carboniferous. [From Leclercq and
Banks, 1962.]

more primitive early Devonian plants to the later fern groups and the pteridosperms.

The Belgian quarry where *P. nodosus* was found has also produced a fossil
that may be an early articulate—*Calamophyton bicephalum.* It is known from
dichotomously branching shoots with a main axis of about 2 cm in diameter

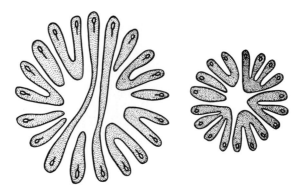

FIG. 7–6. *Pseudosporochnus nodosus,* restoration diagrams of the cross-sectional form of the xylem in the first- and second-order branches. [From Leclercq and Banks, 1962.]

(Fig. 7–7). The basal part of the plant has not been found, and consequently the overall size is not known. The sterile appendages ("leaves") are three-dimensional structures (Fig. 7–8) that branch in two planes and were probably terete in cross section. The fertile appendages, which are confined to special branchlets, are rather complex (Fig. 7–9). They divide shortly beyond the point of attachment into two essentially identical parts, each of which bears three branches with two terminal sporangia each, and the forks of the appendage terminate in a dichotomy.

In the tendency for the appendages of *Calamophyton* to be somewhat whorled, and in the structure of the fertile ones, the plant seems to be most closely aligned with the earlier members of the articulates, of which *Equisetum* is the only surviving genus. Specimens with internal structure have not as yet been studied, and they may shed significant light on the correct affinities of *Calamophyton.* The fossils that have already been assigned, tentatively or otherwise, to the Devonian and Carboniferous articulates include a diverse assemblage, and the variety will probably increase as our knowledge expands.

LATE DEVONIAN PLANTS THAT SEEM TO SHED LIGHT ON PTERIDOPHYTE-GYMNOSPERM TRANSITION

In 1960 Beck suggested the inclusion of certain problematical fossils under the new group name Progymnospermopsida. Three orders with eight genera were assigned to the group. The degree to which the eight genera of plants is known varies considerably, and I have selected three that seem to represent the typical characteristics of these plants as far as they are known. Perhaps the most important features are large compound leaves (or structures that have been interpreted as such), sporangiate reproduction (they were pteridophytic), and a strong development of secondary wood. Beck has noted ". . . it is very likely that they comprise the ancestral complex from which the major groups

FIG. 7–7. *Calamophyton bicephalum* from the mid-Devonian of Belgium, a primitive pteridophyte that may be an early member of the articulate group. The main axis is about 2 cm broad. [From Leclercq and Andrews, 1960.]

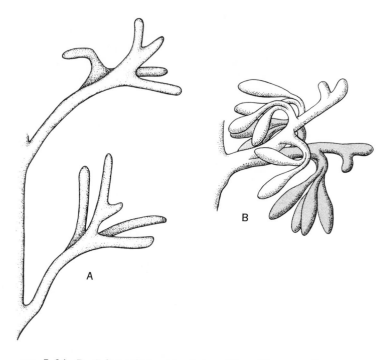

FIG. 7–8A, B. *Calamophyton bicephalum*. The ultimate sterile appendages (leaves) and a fertile appendage, enlarged. [From Leclercq and Andrews, 1960.]

of gymnosperms evolved." This may not meet with complete agreement, but it does seem safe to assert that some highly significant leads are contributing to a general understanding of the pteridophyte-gymnosperm transition.

Archaeopteris and *Callixylon* are genera that have attracted special attention in the past few years. The former is based on fernlike fronds from widespread localities in the Upper Devonian of north temperate and Arctic latitudes. The fronds reach a maximum length of about one meter; the primary branches or pinnae bear two rows of pinnules that are essentially wedge-shaped in outline, and in different species they range from entire or nearly so to very finely dissected. Certain pinnae, often the basal ones, were fertile. Their organization seems to have been identical with that of the sterile ones, but in place of the more or less laminate structure, several stalked sporangia were borne on the rachis of the pinnule.

Only a few of the twenty-five or more described species of *Archaeopteris* are at all well known; perhaps the most interesting is *A. latifolia* from the Upper Devonian of Pennsylvania (Arnold, 1939). This was probably a heterosporous plant. Two kinds of sporangia were borne on the fertile pinnules, both of which are 2 mm long; some sporangia were about .3 mm in diameter and others were about .5 mm in diameter. These attached sporangia had shed their spores, but closely associated ones in the surrounding matrix revealed eight to sixteen spores, each 300 microns in diameter in the larger sporangia, and in the smaller ones there were many more spores, each about 35 microns in diameter.

More recently J. M. Pettitt has reported (Chaloner and Pettitt, 1964) finding fertile specimens of *Archaeopteris jacksoni* Arnold from Scaumenac Bay, Quebec, in which the sporangia contain either nine to forty-eight megaspores that range from 200 to 270 microns in diameter, or several hundred microspores that are 45 to 70 microns in diameter.

In the summer of 1962, in collaboration with N. W. Radforth and T. L. Phillips, I collected *Archaeopteris* specimens from Ellesmere Island in the Canadian Arctic. Some of the sporangia borne on our specimens contain spores 60 microns in diameter, and we estimate the number per sporangium to have been well over a thousand. We found much larger spores, probably megaspores, in the surrounding matrix although we cannot be certain that they were produced by the same plants.

A great deal of interest has centered around the morphology of the *Archaeopteris* frond, but only very recently has any information been available on its anatomy. At meetings of the Botanical Society of America, Carluccio (1963) presented evidence to suggest that the vascular supply of the rachis is a radially symmetrical stele. There is thus a distinct possibility that the structure we have regarded as a frond may be a specialized branch system in which the "pinnules" are the real fronds. This, however, is hardly beyond the speculative stage at present.

Occupying much the same geographic and stratigraphic range, the genus *Callixylon*, like *Archaeopteris*, has long been known from the Upper Devonian and is represented by several species. It is based on petrified stems in which the primary bundles arranged around the periphery of the pith are mesarch and the secondary wood is of the coniferous type, consisting of tracheids and rays; the latter are usually not more than two cells broad. A feature regarded as especially diagnostic of *Callixylon* is the grouping of the pits in the radial walls of the tracheids. *Callixylon* stems attained a great size by any standards in the plant kingdom. Arnold has described a specimen from Indiana three feet in diameter, and trunks of five feet have been reported from Oklahoma.

Callixylon was long regarded as a seed plant by many botanists, although the seeds have never been found! It was, therefore, a discovery of great interest when Beck (1960a, 1960b) announced finding *Archaeopteris* fronds attached to a stem about 3 cm in diameter which displayed the distinctive wood anatomy of *Callixylon*. The identity of the two seems to be clearly established in this case. We thus have a stem with gymnospermous type of wood (characteristic of the conifers) bearing appendages that for lack of more appropriate terminology one is tempted to call fernlike. The plant combines classical gymnospermous and pteridophyte features. However, it cannot be called a fern or even fernlike with any real degree of accuracy. Furthermore, it had not attained the seed habit and cannot be called a gymnosperm. This is a great step forward, but it seems fair to add that we are really just beginning to learn something about *Archaeopteris*. Many questions remain: Were the fronds of all species borne on *Callixylon* stems? Were they all heterosporous, and if so to what degree?

Tetraxylopteris schmidtii is another interesting fossil assigned by Beck (1957) to his Progymnospermopsida. The restoration (Fig. 7–9) shows the known

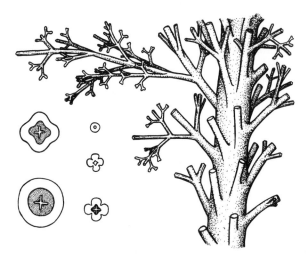

FIG. 7–9. *Tetraxylopteris schmidtii,* an Upper Devonian plant from New York. Part of the stem is shown with the basal portions of several of the spirally arranged fronds. The figures at the left are transverse diagrams from different branch orders of the frond as indicated by the letters. The stipple indicates secondary vascular tissue. [From Beck, 1957, redrawn.]

parts of the plant. The central axis, presumed to be the stem, attained a diameter of 2.5 cm and bore spirally arranged appendages interpreted as fronds. The central axis of the frond in turn bears decussately arranged primary branches, thus producing a three-dimensional structure. The primary branches give rise to comparably oriented secondary ones, and the ultimate divisions are dichotomous branchlets that show no evidence of any lamination. Little is known about the anatomy of the stem, but fragmentary portions of the rachis as well as its primary and secondary branches are preserved and include a four-lobed core of primary wood enclosed in secondary wood. The latter consists of tracheids pitted on all walls and of rays that vary from one to several cells broad. The distal portions of certain fronds bore sporangia that were arranged in rather dense clusters. The sporangia were quite large, being 2.5 to 5 mm long and

.5 to .8 mm wide; they were probably without a distinct annulus, and no information is available on the spores. In his original account of the plant Beck points to certain characters as suggesting pteridosperm affinities: the presence of secondary wood, the round bordered pits of the tracheids, and a sclerotic outer cortex. Suggestive of fern (or pteridophyte) affinities are the large clustered sporangia and the three-dimensional branching of the fronds.

Several genera of Devonian plants have been described with essentially fan-shaped leaves. It seems appropriate to introduce one of them here as indicative of the complexity of the evolutionary stages that led to the seed plants. It may be transitional between the pteridophytic and gymnosperm levels, but it is not implied that it is in any way fernlike. Described under the name *Ginkgophyton* sp. (Beck, 1963), the plant is known from Upper Devonian fossils of New York that consist of partially petrified axes bearing fan-shaped leaves that probably attained a maximum length of 10 cm. The axis (Fig. 7–10) includes a

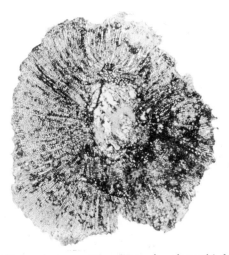

FIG. 7–10. *Ginkgophyton*, an Upper Devonian plant with fan-shaped leaves; the axis, which has strongly developed secondary wood, is shown here enlarged fifteen times. *Ginkgophyton* may represent a distinct group of plants transitional between pteriodphytes and gymnosperms. [From Beck, *Science*, Vol. 141 (1963), cover.]

pith with several peripheral strands of primary wood; this is surrounded by secondary xylem of tracheids and narrow rays, the tracheids having alternate circular bordered pits. We thus have a strong suggestion of gymnospermy in the stem anatomy, but the leaf structure indicates a plant probably quite different from *Archaeopteris* or *Tetraxylopteris*.

Other Devonian plants have been described with fan-shaped leaves, although it is not known whether they are at all closely related. *Psygmophyllum gilkineti* Leclercq (19) from the Middle Devonian of Belgium consists of a branching stem fragment (impression) about 20 cm long that bore twenty-two leaves, each one consisting of an elongate petiole up to 33 cm long which expanded into a wedge-shaped blade 10 to 14 cm long and of about the same breadth.

Enigmophyton superbum Höeg (19) from the late Devonian of Spitsbergen has fan-shaped leaves attached to a slender dichotomizing axis. Heterosporous fructifications, slightly suggestive of a lycopod cone, were associated with it.

SOME EVIDENCE BEARING ON THE EARLY EVOLUTION OF SEED PLANTS

There has been considerable speculation concerning the existence of seed plants in pre-Carboniferous times, but to the best of my knowledge no positive evidence of them has been discovered. However, an interesting candidate exists in a recent discovery from Upper Devonian rocks of Quebec; this is *Cystosporites* (Chaloner and Pettitt, 1963, 1964), a spore tetrad isolated from sandstone (Fig. 7–11). Each tetrad includes one large, and presumably functional, oval-shaped

FIG. 7–11. An Upper Devonian megaspore, *Cystosporites* sp. The spore tetrad is shown at the left; the large functional megaspore is 2.5 mm long. The distal part of the large spore, and the three small abortive spores, are shown at the right. [From Chaloner and Pettitt, 1963.]

megaspore over 2 mm long (the largest one found measures 2,550 microns) and three abortive spores of approximately 150 microns in diameter. The parent plant is not known, but the authors suggest that the fossil most likely represents a lycopod of the lepidocarp group. Certain lycopods of the Pennsylvania evolved into seed plants in the sense that the sporangium became enclosed—except for a narrow slit (micropyle) along the top—and the number of functional mega-spores in a megasporangium became reduced to one.

Archaeopteris has been found at the Quebec (Scaumenac Bay) locality where *Cystosporites* was obtained. Chaloner and Pettitt point out that it is at least conceivable that the latter could be the megaspore of a plant of the *Archaeopteris* type. In any event the tetrad, with one huge functional spore, presents a more advanced level of heterospory than was previously known from the Devonian.

During the past century or more, a good deal of study and thought have gone into attempts to understand the origin of the seed in gymnospermous plants and the seed pod or carpel of the flowering plants. Thus one of the most exciting developments in vascular plant evolution centers around the recent discovery of very primitive seeds and seed-bearing organs, much of this resulting from the researches of of A. G. Long (1961, and other papers cited therein).*

In recent decades several botanists have suggested that the integument evolved from a ring of filaments or branches of one sort or another that became fused together. Long's discoveries offer abundant support to the theory. *Genomosperma kidstoni* (Fig. 7–12A) from the Lower Carboniferous of Scotland is a very primitive seed in which the nucellus is enclosed by eight filaments that are separate down to the base. There is no micropyle as the filaments (integument) flare outward.

In *Genomosperma latens* (Fig. 7–12B) the integumentary lobes are fused from the base for about a third of their length and are closely appressed at the distal end, forming at least a rudimentary micropyle.

Physostoma elegans (Fig. 7–12D), an Upper Carboniferous seed, shows a somewhat more advanced degree of fusion of the integument lobes and, in two more of Long's Lower Carboniferous seeds (*Eurystoma angulare,* Fig. 7–12E; *Stamnostoma huttonense,* Fig. 7–12F), fusion is almost or wholly complete.

Some of the Lower Carboniferous seeds developed a considerable degree of specialization; for example, *Salpingostoma dasu* (Fig. 7–12C) is elongate and spindle-shaped with an overall length of 50 mm and a maximum diameter of 6 mm. The integument, above the level of the distal part of the nucellus, is divided into five or six slender tentacle-like lobes whose basal portions enclose the elongate, tubular, and slightly flaring *salpinx*. The salpinx, a specialized distal portion of the nucellus, offers a significant sidelight on the evolution of certain seeds usually referred to the Pteridosperms. In seeds such as *Stamnostoma huttonense* and *Eurystoma angulare* (Fig. 7–13A, E), where a micropyle is lacking, it seems likely that the strongly developed salpinx would have been of signifi-cant aid in directing the pollen into the pollen chamber. The case is less clear in

---

* Grateful acknowledgement is due to *Science* for permission to reproduce parts of my article on "Early Seed Plants" from the November 15, 1963, issue. What follows has largely been taken from that article.

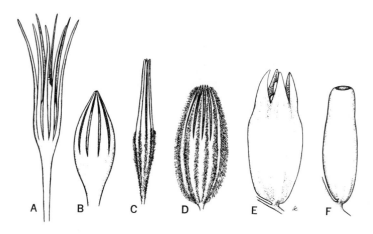

FIG. 7–12A–F. Some seeds attributed to the pteridosperms that show variation in the degree of fusion of the integument lobes and in the presence or absence of a micropyle. (A) *Genomosperma kidstoni* (Calder) Long; seed length approximately 15 mm. (B) *Genomosperma latens* Long; seed length, 8 mm. (C) *Salpingostoma dasu* Gordon; seed length, 50 mm. (D) *Physostoma elegans* Williamson; seed length, 6 mm. (E) *Eurystoma angulare* Long; seed length, 8 mm. (F) *Stamnostoma huttonense* Long; seed length, 3.7 mm. [From Andrews, *Science,* Vol. 142 (1963); redrawn from Long and other sources.]

Salpingostoma dasu (Fig. 7–13B) where the greatly elongated distal extremities of the integument serve no obvious purpose, but in which the pollen, once it was within the long micropylar tube, would have been directed into the pollen chamber by the lining of hairs and the trumpet-shaped salpinx.

It may be emphasized again that the seeds, or distinctive portions of them, shown in Fig. 7–12A–F do not necessarily constitute a straight-line evolutionary series. They do represent significant stages in the envelopment of the nucellus by a ring of vegetative lobes which later fused together to form a nearly completely enclosing integument, and in some seeds this integument became organically fused to the nucellus, to a greater or lesser degree.

Several seeds attributed to the pteridosperms are known to have been enveloped, singly or in groups and to a greater or lesser degree, in a structure known as the cupule. Its importance lies in the strong suggestion that it may be homologous with the carpel (seed pod) of the flowering plants. Figure 7–14A–E illustrates certain phases in the evolution of the cupule; but in the case of several of the fossils, little is known of the rest of the plant, and here again there is no implication of a direct evolutionary sequence.

Tyliosperma orbiculatum (Fig. 7–14C) is known from small, nearly spherical seeds about 3.7 mm long. The integument and nucellus are united except at

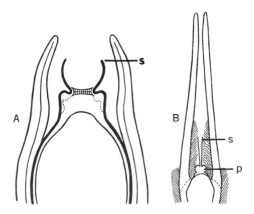

FIG. 7–13A, B. The distal end of two pteridosperm seeds, in median longitudinal section, showing modifications of the tip of the nucellus to form pollen chamber (p) and salpinx (s). (A) *Eurystoma angulare*. (B) *Salpingostoma dasu*. [(A) from Long; (B) from Gordon.]

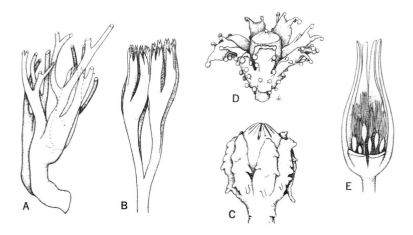

FIG. 7–14A–E. Some seed-bearing organs attributed to the pteridosperms, showing variations in the degree of fusion of the cupule lobes. (A) *Eurystoma angulare;* dotted line indicates position of the seed. (B) *Stamnostoma huttonense;* dotted line indicates position of one seed. (C) *Tyliosperma orbiculatum* Mamay. (D) *Lyginopteris oldhamia*. (E) *Calathospermum scoticum* Walton. [(A), (B) from Long; (C) from Mamay; (D) from Oliver and Scott; (E) from Walton.]

the apical end of the seed, where the integument is divided into seven free lobes. What the vascularization (conducting system) of the seed was is uncertain; but there were probably seven strands, and they are thought to have been confined to the nucellus rather than to the integument. The seed is, in turn, partially enclosed by seven or eight fleshy segments, free for the greater part of their length, which compose the cupule.

The seed by which others in the pteridosperm group have been judged is one described originally under the name *Lagenostoma lomaxi,* from the Upper Carboniferous of Britain. In 1904 Oliver and Scott demonstrated that this is the female organ of *Lyginopteris oldhamia,* a vine-like pteridosperm with rather primitive, fernlike foliage. The seed (Fig. 7–14D) is barrel-shaped, about 5.5 mm long, and a little over 4 mm in diameter.

The integument and nucellus are united for about four-fifths the length of the seed, and the integument is slightly lobed in the distal free part. The extreme tip of the pollen chamber projects slightly through the micropyle. The cupule consists of about eight segments united for approximately half their length. The vascular strands at the base of the cupule branch several times. The exact number of these strands is not clear, but from Oliver and Scott's description it appears that each cupule lobe was supplied with more than one bundle, and this may mean there were originally more than eight cupule segments. Rather abundant, large, and essentially spherical glands are a conspicuous feature of the fossil.

Several multiseeded cupules have been reported; the largest of them is *Calathospermum* from the Lower Carboniferous of Scotland. The cupule of *C. scoticum* Walton (Fig. 7–14E) is a tulip-shaped organ of six broad lobes. These are basally united, and there are five or six vascular strands in each. Several dozen seeds, each at the tip of a slender stalk, are borne within the cupule. Several cupules contain only stalks—a finding that indicates that the seeds were extruded and separated from the distal end of the stalk as they approached maturity. The seeds are similar if not identical to those described independently under the name *Salpingostoma dasu.*

More recently Barnard has described another species, *Calathospermum fimbriatum,* which has several features of special interest. The cupule is about 90 mm long, and it is thought that it was borne terminally on the primary rachis of a special fertile frond. It differs from *C. scoticum* in the greater division of its cupule wall; each of the two primary halves of the wall divides into three segments near the base, and each segment in turn divides into five branches or pinnae, some of which were sterile and others seed-bearing.

The most primitive cupulate organ found to date—so rudimentary that there is some question whether it should be called a cupule—is that of *Eurystoma angulare* (Fig. 7–14A). The seed is roughly embraced by a system of dichotomizing terete branches that may represent a slightly specialized portion of a primitive frond. The view that this branch system does represent an early stage in the development of a cupule is supported by Long's discovery of *Stamnostoma huttonense* (Fig. 7–14B), also from the Lower Carboniferous. A common stalk bears a pair of cupules, each of which was formed by two divisions (at right angles to each other) of the initial branch system; these four main branches of each cupule fork toward the distal extremity, with as many as sixteen terminal divisions. Scars where other seeds may have been attached suggest that each cupule may have contained as many as four seeds.

In *S. huttonense* the enclosing branchlets are organized into a more definite entity than in *Eurystoma*, and the fossil seems to represent an intermediate stage between the latter and the more highly evolved pteridosperms such as *Tyliosperma* and *Calathospermum*.

We have little information concerning the way in which the cupules were borne on the plants as a whole, but a few fossils reveal something of their group organization. Some years ago Benson described *Calathiops bernhardti* as a simple pinnate branch system in which each primary division produced several branchlets that terminated in what seemed to be a multiseeded structure. At least *Calathiops* was so interpreted, and recent discoveries substantiate this opinion. Each cupule is a little over 3 cm long and contained perhaps a dozen seeds. There is a basic similarity to Walton's *Calathospermum*, but the cupule of *Calathiops* is smaller, with fewer seeds, and there are more divisions.

In *Calathospermum fimbriatum* there appears to have been one large terminal cupule on a special (?) frond, and Barnard suggests that the two major divisions may be homologous with primary divisions of the main rachis (central axis) of the leaf or frond. This bifurcation of the main rachis of the frond is characteristic of several pteridosperms, and it seems probable that Barnard is correct.

Among his other contributions Long has described some compression fossils that he identified with petrified cupules and seeds of *Stamnostoma huttonense* that he had described earlier. The compressions consist of bifurcating axes, with cupules usually borne in pairs at the distal extremities; some of them contained at least two seeds.

I have tried to outline some of the more interesting contributions of the past few years that have materially advanced our understanding of pteridophyte evolution and the origin of the gymnosperms. Activity in this area of paleo-botanical investigation has lately shown a marked increase; it seems especially encouraging that several able investigators are attacking, with marked success, problems that have long concerned all biologists who have a serious interest in the origin and development of plants. In view of the small but growing number of researchers on this particular frontier and the great advances made, it is fair to note that this phase of "modern biology" has outstripped most others, and it will continue to do so, judging by the investigations presently under way.

REFERENCES

ANDREWS, H. N. "Early Seed Plants." *Science*, Vol. 142 (1963), pp. 925–931.

BARNARD, P. D. W. "*Calathospermum fimbriatum* sp. nov., a Lower Carboniferous Pteridosperm Cupule from Scotland." *Palaeontology*, Vol. 3, No. 3 (1960), pp. 265–275.

BECK, C. B. "*Tetraxylopteris schmidtii* gen. et sp. nov., a Probable Pteridosperm Precursor from the Devonian of New York." *American Journal of Botany*, Vol. 44 (1957), pp. 350–367.

———. "The Identity of *Archaeopteris* and *Callixylon*." *Brittonia*, Vol. 12, No. 4 (1960), pp. 351–368.

———. "Reconstructions of *Archaeopteris*, and Further Consideration of its Phylogenetic Position." *American Journal of Botany*, Vol. 49 (1962), pp. 373–382.

———. "*Ginkgophyton (Psygmophyllum)* with a Stem of Gymnospermic Structure." *Science*, Vol. 141 (1963), pp. 431–432.

BENSON, M. "The Fructification, *Calathiops Bernhardti*, n. sp." *Annals of Botany*, Vol. 49 (1935), pp. 155–160.

CARLUCCIO, L. "Remarks on *Archaeopteris*." *American Journal of Botany*, Vol. 50 (1963), p. 627.

CHALONER, W. G., AND J. M. PETTITT. "A Devonian Seed Megaspore." *Nature*, Vol. 198 (1963), pp. 808–809.

HOEG, O. A. "The Downtonian and Devonian Flora of Spitsbergen." *Norges Svalbard-og Ishavs-Undersøkeleser*, Skrifter Nr. 83 (1942), pp. 1–228.

KRAUSEL, R. "*Paulophyton jongmansi* n. sp., eine Pflanze altertümlichen Baues aus dem Namur des Ruhrgebietes." *Mededelingen van de Geologische Stichting*, N.S.,Vol.11 (1957), pp. 21–25.

LECLERCQ, S. "*Psygmophyllum Gilkineti*, sp. n., du Devonien Moyen a Facies Old Red Sandstone de Malonne (Environs de Namur, Belgique)." *Journal of the Linnean Society of London* (Botany), Vol. 48 (1928), pp. 1–14.

———, AND H. N. ANDREWS. "*Calamophyton bicephalum*, a New Species from the Middle Devonian of Belgium." *Annals of the Missouri Botanical Gardens*, Vol. 47 (1960), pp. 1–18.

———, AND H. P. BANKS. "*Pseudosporochnus nodosus* sp. nov., a Middle Devonian Plant with Cladoxylalean Affinities." *Palaeontographica*, Vol. 110B (1962), pp. 1–34.

LONG, A. G. "*Tristichia ovensi* gen. et sp. nov., a Protostelic Lower Carboniferous Pteridosperm, etc." *Transactions of the Royal Society of Edinburgh*, Vol. 64 (1961), pp. 477–489.

MAMAY, S. H. "Two New Plant Genera of Pennsylvania Age from Kansas Coal Balls." *U.S. Geological Survey Professional Papers*, 254-D (1954), pp. 81–95.

OBRHEL, J. "Ein Landpflanzenfund in Mittelböhmischen Ordovizium." *Geologie*, Jahr. 8, Heft 5 (1959), pp. 535–541.

———. "Die Flora der Pridoli-Schichten (Budnany-Stufe) des Mittelbohmischen Silurs." *Geologie*, Jahr. 11, Heft 1 (1962), pp. 83–96.

OLIVER, F. W., AND D. H. SCOTT. "On the Structure of the Palaeozoic Seed *Lagenostoma lomaxi*, etc." *Philosophical Transactions of the Royal Society of London*, Vol. 197B (1904), pp. 193–247.

ROSELT, G. "Ober die Ältesten Landpflanzen und eine Mögliche Landpflanze aus dem Ludlow Sachsens." *Geologie*, Jahr. 11, Heft 3 (1962), pp. 320–333.

ELECTRON TRANSPORT SYSTEMS IN PLANTS

8

Walter D. Bonner, Jr.

Johnson Foundation
University of Pennsylvania

Living organisms utilize the energy contained in the phosphate bonds of adenosine triphosphate (ATP) to drive reactions that lead to maintenance and growth of their cells, tissues, and organs. Adenosine triphosphate is produced from adenosine diphosphate (ADP) by processes involved in fermentation, aerobic respiration, and photosynthesis. Almost all of the reactions involved in these processes can be described in molecular terms since, in a sense, cells are molecular engines. Heat produced during respiration or photosynthesis is lost to cells because they are unable to use heat to perform useful work. Hence, cells have developed mechanisms to conserve energy within chemical bonds and to use the energy released in the degradation of these chemical bonds to perform work. This article describes the present knowledge of some of the reactions involved in energy conservation (as ATP bond energy) in both aerobic cellular respiration and in photosynthesis.

Cells convert carbohydrates in the process of glycolysis into pyruvic acid. During the glycolytic formation of pyruvic acid, only a small portion of the total energy present in the carbohydrate molecule is liberated to the cells as ATP; most of the energy of the carbohydrate resides in pyruvic acid, two molecules of which are produced for each six-carbon carbohydrate utilized. In the cells of aerobic organisms, pyruvic acid loses one carbon atom by decarboxylation, and is converted into the substance acetyl co-enzyme A. The metabolism of fat similarly produces acetyl co-enzyme A through the processes involved in the degradation of fatty acids by beta oxidation. Once formed, acetyl co-enzyme A can combine with oxaloacetic acid, forming the six-carbon compound citric acid and co-enzyme A. The formation of citric acid from acetyl co-enzyme A and oxalo-acetic acid proceeds in a very complicated series of reactions that initiates the Krebs tri-carboxylic acid cycle.

One of the basic reactions that occurs in the Krebs cycle as well as in

135

glycolysis is the oxidation of specific substances by the removal of hydrogen atoms. Such oxidations are carried out by enzymes called dehydrogenases. For example, succinic acid is oxidized by the enzyme succinic dehydrogenase to fumaric acid in the reaction:

$$
\begin{array}{c}
\text{COOH} \\
| \\
\text{CH}_2 \\
| \\
\text{CH}_2 \\
| \\
\text{COOH}
\end{array}
\quad
\begin{array}{c}
\xrightarrow{\ \ \ \text{succinic}\ \ \ } \\
\xleftarrow{\ \ \ \text{dehydrogenase}\ \ \ }
\end{array}
\quad
\begin{array}{c}
\text{COOH} \\
| \\
\text{CH} \\
|| \\
\text{CH} \\
| \\
\text{COOH}
\end{array}
$$

Oxidations of this type require a hydrogen acceptor, in addition to the dehydrogenase enzyme. In the cells of aerobic organisms, the final hydrogen acceptor is oxygen. And during the transfer of hydrogen atoms or their equivalents from the compound being oxidized to oxygen, the bulk of the energy produced in cellular respiration is conserved as chemical bond energy in ATP.

A general expression for the oxidation of organic compounds by the removal of hydrogen atoms is:

$$AH_2 + B \longrightarrow A + BH_2$$

In this expression, A becomes oxidized by donating its hydrogen atoms to B; consequently, B becomes reduced. If the concentration of AH_2 is unlimited and that of B limited and small compared to A, the reaction will proceed only as long as free B is available. When all of B is converted to BH_2, the reaction will cease unless some means of reconverting BH_2 into B is provided. One such means would be to provide a second hydrogen atom acceptor, C, that reacts with BH_2; and if the concentration of C was limiting, one could provide a third hydrogen acceptor, D, and so on, until a hydrogen acceptor, E, present in unlimited amounts, is reached. The important feature of such a system is that the final hydrogen acceptor be present in excess and can be a sink for the disposal of the hydrogen atoms. Using a series of hydrogen acceptors, the expression for the oxidation of the AH_2 now becomes:

In short, AH_2 is oxidized through a hydrogen transport system. The situation is more complex in cellular respiration, but cells do possess mechanisms, in principle, similar to that described for the oxidation of substrates by the transport of hydrogen atoms, or transport of electrons, from the substrates of respiration to oxygen, the final acceptor in the system.

Although the dehydrogenases accomplish oxidations of organic compounds by the removal of hydrogen atoms, the transport systems in cells are designed only partly for hydrogen transport. The transport of electrons by means of special electron carriers plays the principal role in cellular oxidations, energy conservation, and the final reaction of the cell with oxygen. The electrons are derived from the hydrogen atoms according to the reaction:

$$H \longrightarrow H^+ + e$$

The principal hydrogen or electron carriers in cells are of three kinds: diphosophopyridine nucleotide (DPN+), flavoproteins, and cytochromes. Cytochromes were discovered in 1925 by David Keilin.* In his elegant and classical paper, Keilin described three cytochromes, which he named cytochromes *a, b,* and *c.* He also presented evidence showing that these cytochromes played an intimate role in cell respiration. We now know a rather large number of cytochromes. They are classified partly on a chemical basis and partly on spectral properties as *a*-type, *b*-type, or *c*-type cytochromes.

Cytochromes are iron-porphyrinproteins, or hemoproteins. They contain a tetrapyrrol structure, a structure common to hemoglobin and to chlorophyll; this structure is shown in Fig. 8–1. Cytochromes differ from each other in the

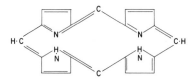

FIG. 8–1. Tetrapyrrol structure.

nature of porphyrin, the substituents on the porphyrin ring, the protein, and in the numbers of porphyrin rings associated with protein. Cytochrome *c* has been highly purified and its structure subjected to careful study. Figure 8–2 illustrates the basic structure of cytochrome *c* as it is now understood.

An important feature of the cytochromes is that the iron imbedded in the porphyrin ring can be oxidized or reduced—that is, they can either donate an electron to a suitable electron acceptor or receive an electron from a suitable electron donor. This feature of oxidation or reduction enables these cytochromes to act as carriers in electron transport systems. Another feature of the cytochromes is that their absorption spectra depend on the state of oxidation of the iron. In the oxidized form, cytochromes show negligible absorption in the visible spectrum, but when reduced, they show a remarkably sharp and strong absorption (Fig. 8–3).

In the mitochondria, cellular respiration occurs: substrates are oxidized, hydrogen atoms (or electrons) are transported to oxygen, and the energy of substrate oxidation is conserved in a form useful for cell work. Most present-day know-

---

* Keilin's 1925 paper is reprinted in Gabriel and Fogel (eds.), *Great Experiments in Biology* (Englewood Cliffs, N.J.: Prentice-Hall, Inc., 1955).

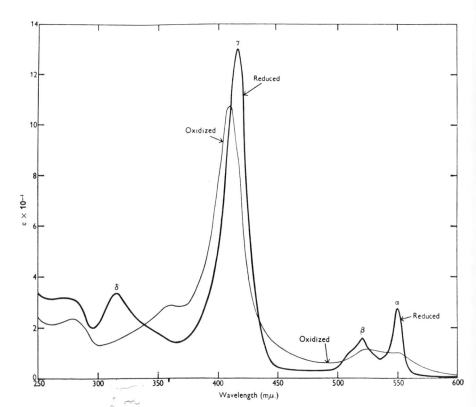

FIG. 8–2. Structure of cytochrome *c*.

FIG. 8–3. Absorption spectra of oxidized and reduced cytochrome *c*.

ledge of these processes has been obtained from studies of isolated liver or heart mitochondria (Fig. 8–4).

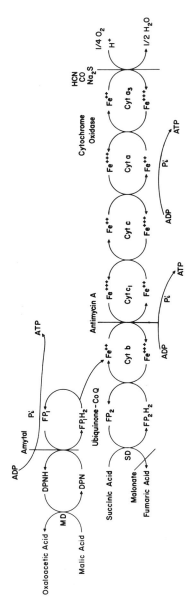

FIG. 8–4. Schematic representation of hydrogen and electron transport to oxygen following the oxidation of succinic acid to fumaric acid and of malic acid to oxoloacetic acid. The sequence of events has been described in animal liver and heart mitochondria.

Succinic acid is oxidized to fumaric acid in the presence of the enzyme succinic dehydrogenase by the removal of two hydrogen atoms. The acceptor for these hydrogen atoms is a flavoprotein (FP_2) which then becomes reduced flavoprotein (FP_2H_2). Reoxidation of FP_2H_2 is accomplished by this carrier, donating two electrons, one at a time, to cytochrome b and by the simultaneous release of two protons. The reduced cytochrome b so produced is reoxidized in turn by donating its electron to cytochrome c_1, producing reduced cytochrome c_1. This process of alternate reduction and reoxidation proceeds along the chain until, in a very complex reaction, the electrons from the cytochrome oxidase are utilized to reduce oxygen to water. Some of the free protons released earlier in this process are required for this reaction, which may be represented in the following equation:

$$4\,Fe^{++} + O_2 + 4\,H^+ \longrightarrow 4\,Fe^{+++} + 2\,H_2O$$

As long as succinate is continually produced and as long as the oxygen supply is not limiting, the reaction can proceed indefinitely. If the oxygen supply is depleted, the final electron acceptor is abolished, and all of the cytochromes will become reduced. If, on the other hand, the succinic acid supply becomes exhausted, and even though there is an ample oxygen supply, there will be no wave of reducing power or electrons proceeding along the chain, and all of the cytochromes will remain oxidized. In the upper left-hand corner of Fig. 8–4, the oxidation of malic acid to oxaloacetic acid is shown. This oxidation is accomplished again by the removal of two hydrogen atoms in the presence of the enzyme malic dehydrogenase. These two hydrogen atoms, in the form of one hydrogen atom, one electron, and one free proton, are received by diphosphopyridine nucleotide (DPN+), producing reduced diphosphopyridine nucleotide (DPNH). The reoxidation of DPNH to DPN+ is accomplished by hydrogen and electron transfer to a flavoprotein, FP_1, which then becomes reduced to FP_1H_2. Again the FP_1H_2 is reoxidized by donating an electron to cytochrome b, and the processes as outlined for succinic acid continues. Not only succinic acid and malic acid are oxidized in the manner shown; all of the oxidations that occur in the Krebs cycle take place in the mitochondria and involve hydrogen and electron transport in a similar manner. The transport of electrons to oxygen does not happen spontaneously. Many processes in biology proceed along a gradient; in the case of the electron transport system, it is a gradient that can be expressed in terms of oxidation-reduction potentials. There are precise relationships between oxidation-reduction potentials and potential energy, and it is possible to calculate the difference in energy between different pairs of electron transport carriers. A consequence of such calculations shows that during the oxidation of malic acid, there is sufficient energy available to produce three molecules of adenosine triphosphate (ATP) from three molecules of adenosine diphosphate (ADP) and three molecules of inorganic phosphate (P_i).

The approximate places where the phosphorylation of ADP to ATP takes place in the respiratory chain are indicated in Fig. 8–4.

Various inhibitors of cell respiration have proven most useful in studying the respiratory chain; some of these inhibitors and their sites of action are indicated in Fig. 8–4. Compounds like cyanide, sulfide, and carbon monoxide are well-known poisons of respiration; they inhibit by blocking the reaction between cytochrome oxidase and oxygen. Since the inhibition is rather specific, the electrons from substrate will proceed down the chain to the point of inhibition; and in the presence of these inhibitors, all of the cytochromes become reduced. Another effective inhibitor of respiration is the substance antimycin A, which acts by blocking electron transfer between cytochrome b and cytochrome c_1. In the presence of antimycin A, all the cytochromes on the oxygen side of this block will be oxidized, while those on the substrate side will be reduced. Other inhibitors are amytal and similar narcotics, which inhibit DPNH oxidation, and malonate, a specific inhibitor of succinic dehydrogenase.

In the respiratory chain, as illustrated in Fig. 8–4, complete oxidation or complete reduction of cytochromes is found under certain very specific conditions—for example, the absence of substrate or absence of oxygen. During oxidation of substrates, the cytochromes are only partially reduced in the presence of oxygen, and the amount of this reduction will depend on a variety of conditions. For example, some substrates are oxidized more rapidly than others; the more rapid the oxidation, the greater the wave of reducing power traveling down the chain and the more reduced are the cytochromes. Since there are many different substrates, each of varying rates of oxidation, there can exist many different levels of cytochrome reduction; a given persisting level of cytochrome reduction may be called a steady state. There can be a great number of steady states in the respiratory chain, each one dependent on some specific factor. Steady state conditions existing in mitochondria will be discussed again below.*

It has generally been assumed that the electron transport system in higher plant mitochondria is exactly the same as that described for animal mitochondria, in spite of the fact that there has been very little evidence in support of this assumption. Through the years, however, evidence has indicated that there are important differences between animal and higher plant mitochondria. In almost all instances, the oxygen utilization by animal tissues is inhibited by cyanide and carbon monoxide, while in higher plant tissues there are four types of response to carbon monoxide and cyanide: (1) the respiration is completely inhibited; (2) a maximum of approximately 50 percent inhibition of respiration can be obtained; (3) the rate of respiration is either unaltered or even increased;

---

* The above is a very brief sketch of some pertinent features of animal mitochondrial electron transport systems; the interested reader can find readable and more detailed information in E. E. Conn and P. K. Stumpf, *Outlines of Biochemistry* (New York: John Wiley & Sons, Inc., 1963).

and (4) the respiration changes from sensitive to insensitive on "aging" of various tissues. An example of such "aging" is the white potato tuber *Solanum tuberosum*. The respiration of freshly cut, thin potato tuber slices is very easily inhibited by cyanide or carbon monoxide. If, however, the slices are left in a moist atmosphere for a few hours, the respiration changes from one sensitive to cyanide and carbon monoxide to one that is completely insensitive. It is probable that a given tissue or organ will show each of the above four types of response to cyanide or carbon monoxide at some given stage of its morphological development. In addition to the bizarre behavior of higher plant tissues to cyanide and carbon monoxide, the student of plant respiration is now presented with a plethora of cytochromes; no less than sixteen cytochromes have been described in higher plants! Which of these cytochromes participate in mitochondrial electron transport, and what is the mechanism of electron transport to oxygen in the presence of cyanide or carbon monoxide? These two questions can be answered by direct experimental methods.

The first problem in approaching a study of higher plant mitochondrial electron transport is that of isolating mitochondria. It is true that many investigators have been isolating plant mitochondria for a number of years, but it is only very recently that mitochondria that meet the rigorous and generally accepted criteria of intactness have been isolated from higher plant tissues. One criterion of intactness is that the rate of substrate oxidation by isolation mitochondria be governed by the presence or absence of adenosine diphosphate (ADP). It is known that mitochondria that have converted all available ADP to ATP oxidize substrate at a very slow rate. However, when ADP is made available to the mitochondria, the rate of substrate oxidation increases markedly—a unique and interesting feature of the control of mitochondrial oxidations. Figure 8–5 shows the time course of malic acid oxidation by freshly prepared mung bean *(Phaseolus areus)* hypocotyl mitochondria. The figure shows oxygen con-

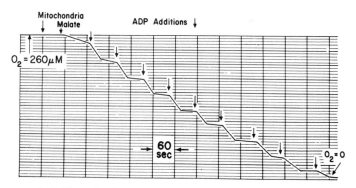

FIG. 8–5. The oxidation of malic acid by mung bean hypocotyl mitochondria. The figure illustrates the control of oxidation rate by the presence or absence of adenosine diphosphate (ADP).

centration, measured by a polarographic method, as a function of time. Addition of the mitochondria causes no appreciable oxygen utilization; the addition of malic acid produces a measurable rate of oxygen utilization; and the addition of a limiting amount of ADP causes an immediate and sharp increase in oxygen utilization that continues until all of the ADP is converted to ATP—then the rate of oxygen utilization decreases to the malic acid rate. This control by ADP of the rate of oxygen utilization can be repeated until the oxygen in the medium is exhausted.

Using good mitochondrial preparations that show such ADP control, one can next make a careful examination of the cytochromes present in mitochondria. One can also compare the cytochromes present in mitochondria that have substrate oxidations insensitive to cyanide and carbon monoxide with mitochondria that have oxidations sensitive to cyanide and carbon monoxide. Such examinations of the mitochondrial cytochromes are most conveniently carried out with the unique sensitive spectrophotometric equipment that has been developed in the laboratories of the Department of Biophysics and Physical Biochemistry at the University of Pennsylvania.

A careful study of mitochondria isolated from a wide variety of plant tissues reveals a remarkable uniformity in the cytochromes present, both in kind and concentration of the cytochromes, but there are some very fundamental differences between plant and animal mitochondria cytochromes. Mitochondria in plant tissues, such as those in liver and heart, contain the cytochromes a and a_3 (cytochrome oxidase); and both types of mitochondria contain cytochrome c, a finding that is not original, since there has been ample evidence for a number of years that plants possess these cytochromes. Plant mitochondria do not contain cytochrome c_1, but there is a cytochrome present that may act in a manner analogous to that of c_1 in animal mitochondria. Animal mitochondria contain one cytochrome b. Those of plants contain three cytochromes b, no one of which is similar to the animal b. In addition, plant mitochondria contain, in small concentration, a cytochrome of the a-type, a cytochrome that can react with oxygen; but this reaction is not inhibited by cyanide or carbon monoxide. The mitochondria from cyanide and carbon-monoxide insensitive tissues appear to have two pathways of electron transport to oxygen, one using cytochrome oxidase, and the other using the newly described a-type cytochrome. In electron transport from substrate to oxygen in the cyanide and carbon-monoxide insensitive mitochondria, ATP is produced from ADP if the electrons pass through cytochrome c and cytochrome oxidase. ATP is not produced if the electrons pass through the alternate pathway; only heat is produced.

The fact that there is no variation in kinds or concentrations of cytochromes present in the mitochondria that have been isolated from many plant species suggests that all plants possess the capacity to exhibit cyanide or carbon-monoxide insensitive respiration or, expressed in another way, to produce heat. The control of the flow of electrons through either an ATP-producing pathway or a heat-producing pathway is an important by-product of the investigations outlined here and, at the present time, represent an unsolved problem. As yet, it is not possible to write a precise electron transport system as it exists in higher plant mitochondria; but one can summarize existing knowledge, as in Fig. 8–6.

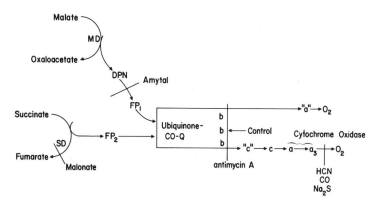

FIG. 8–6. Schematic representation of the respiratory chain in higher plant mitochondria.

In chlorophyll-containing tissues, there exists in the same cells two ATP-generating systems: the mitochondria producing ATP from the controlled oxidation of substrates through hydrogen and electron transport to oxygen (oxygen-activated electron transport), and the chloroplast producing ATP from energy derived from sunlight. Present knowledge of ATP production in the chloroplast, or photophosphorylation as it is called, is very limited. One would expect, however, that the basic mechanisms as we know them in the mitochondria would hold for the phosphorylation of ADP in the chloroplast. That is to say, there must be an electron transport system present in the chloroplast analogous to the one present in mitochondria. Great impetus was given to considering photophosphorylation in such terms when Robert Hill described two cytochromes characteristic of higher plant chloroplasts. These cytochromes are called cytochrome f (for frond) and cytochrome b_6. They are present in the chloroplasts of higher plant green leaves in an equimolar concentration, and there appears to be one molecule of cytochrome f or b_6 for every 200 chlorophyll molecules. It has been difficult to study cytochromes f and b_6 in green leaves or chloroplasts, partly because of the large amount of chlorophyll and carotenoids present but also because of the fact that the instrumentation necessary to make these observations has been developed only recently. The chloroplast cytochromes have not been observed directly as is the case of mitochondrial cytochromes. As a matter of fact, much of our knowledge of these two cytochromes comes from observations made on residues of chloroplasts following removal of chlorophylls and carotenoids with cold 80 percent acetone, a residue incapable of performing any part of the photosynthetic process. Very recently, however, it has been possible to show that cytochrome f changes from its reduced form in the dark to its oxidized form on illumination. That is, there is a light-activated oxidation of cytochrome f, and since this oxidation involves loss of an electron, one can refer to the cytochrome f oxidation as light-activated electron transport. What is truly thrilling about the light-activated oxidation of cytochrome f is that the rate of this oxidation is increased by cooling the green leaf from 25°C to −196°C. Chemical or enzymatic reactions are slowed down by lowering the temperature. At −196°C no chemical reactions proceed in cells; therefore, the temperature-insensitive light-activated oxidation of cytochrome f is a photochemical reaction and probably is a primary photochemical act in the photosynthetic process. The loss of an electron by cytochrome f in a reaction photochemically initiated by energy absorbed by chlorophyll indicates that there must be a very close physical relationship between cytochrome f and chlorophyll, perhaps even a complex between the two molecules. The optical properties of cytochrome f in intact chloroplasts are very different from those of the solubilized and purified cytochrome, an indication that there may well indeed be such a complex.

At the present time, there is no knowledge of the role of cytochrome b_6 in the chloroplast; but one would expect this cytochrome to be part of an electron transport chain. Further developments in the understanding of chloroplast electron transport and phosphorylation will most certainly be exciting ones.

In this article, the present state of knowledge of mitochondrial and chloroplast electron transport systems in higher plants has been sketchily summarized. Considerable progress has been made, especially in the last few years, in the delineation of these systems; and much remains to be done to complete our understanding of the mechanisms of oxygen- and light-activated electron transport and phosphorylation. At the present state of knowledge, however, there are questions one can ask and even begin to investigate. For example, the control of substrate oxidation rate by ADP has been illustrated above. In the green cell, there are present two phosphorylating bodies, each converting ADP to ATP as it is required by the cells and tissues and organs. What is the relationship between these two bodies? Does the amount of ADP or ATP present in one have any influence on the other, or is the chloroplast-produced ATP used completely in the chemical events leading to the reduction of CO_2? This question one can investigate using both isolated chloroplasts and mitochondria; but, so far, such investigations have proven to be rather complex. Knowing the composition of the mitochondrial respiration chain and its cytochromes and their optical properties, one can perform experiments that impose a load on the respiratory chain. We know of many physiological processes that require ATP to drive them. For example, the accumulation and transport of salts by roots require ATP; the ATP being converted to ADP would stimulate the electron transport system. By investigating intact roots in the presence and absence of salt, one could determine the influence of this physiological load on the rate of reactions proceeding in the respiratory chain, and perhaps even begin to have a glimmering of the relationship of how the ATP is expended to drive this physiological process. Other physiological loads that one could impose on whole plants are involved in the transport of water from the roots to the leaves. At the present time, this transport process is explained in physical terms only. There are indications that metabolic energy may be expended on this process, and by investigating the steady state conditions of the components of the respiratory chain, one could certainly approach this vexing problem. Similarly, one could make investigations on the downward translocation of photosynthate. Another interesting problem that could be investigated is the influence of plant growth hormones on the respiratory chain.

It would seem, then, that even with our present state of knowledge concerning these electron transport carriers, many new avenues of investigation are opening up. As our knowledge of these electron transport carriers and the mechanisms of phosphorylation become more complete, a vast number of problems can then be studied concerning the physiology of the whole plant and the control of the energy-producing and energy-consuming systems within the plant. Certainly, at the present time, one can see no shortage of exciting problems for plant physiologists for many, many years to come.

GENERAL REFERENCES

BEEVERS, H. *Respiratory Metabolism in Plants.* New York: Harper & Row, Publishers, 1961.

CONN, E. E., AND P. K. STUMPF. *Outlines of Biochemistry.* New York: John Wiley & Sons, Inc., 1963.

LEHNINGER, A. L. *The Mitochondrion, Molecular Basis of Structure and Function.* New York: W. A. Benjamin, 1964.

SPECIFIC PAPERS AND REVIEWS

BONNER, W. D. JR. "The Cytochromes of Plant Tissues," in *Haematin Enzymes,* eds. J. E. Falk, R. Lemberg, and R. K. Morton. London: Pergamon Press, 1961. Part 2, pp. 479–500.

———. "Cell Respiration and Mitochondria," in *Plant Biochemistry,* eds. J. Bonner and J. Varner. New York: Academic Press, Inc. (in press).

———, AND R. HILL. "Light Induced Optical Changes in Green Leaves," in *Photosynthetic Mechanisms of Green Plants.* Publication 1145, National Academy of Science, 1963. pp. 82–90.

CHANCE, B., AND W. D. BONNER, JR. "The Temperature Insensitive Oxidation of Cytochrome *f* in Green Leaves—A Primary Event of Photosynthesis," in *Photosynthetic Mechanisms of Green Plants.* Publication 1145, National Academy of Science, 1963. pp. 66–81.

GODDARD, D. R., AND W. D. BONNER, JR. "Cellular Respiration," in *Plant Physiology,* ed. F. C. Steward. New York: Academic Press, Inc., 1960. Vol. IA, pp. 209–312.

HACKETT, D. P. "Respiratory Mechanisms and Control in Higher Plant Tissues," in *Control Mechanisms in Respiration and Fermentation,* ed. B. Wright. New York: The Ronald Press Co., 1963. pp. 105–127.

HILL, R., AND W. D. BONNER, JR. "The Nature and Possible Function of Chloroplast Cytochromes," in *Light and Life,* eds. W. D. McElroy and B. Glass. Baltimore: Johns Hopkins Press, 1961. pp. 424–435.

KEILIN, D. "On Cytochrome, a Respiratory Pigment, Common to Animals, Yeast and Higher Plants." *Proceedings of the Royal Society,* Series B, Vol. 98 (1925), p. 312.

————, AND E. C. SLATER. "Cytochrome." *British Medical Bulletin,* Vol. 9 (1953), pp. 89–97.

LIEBERMAN, M., AND J. E. BAKER. "Respiratory Electron Transport." *Annual Revue of Plant Physiology,* Vol. 16 (1965), pp. 343–382.

PARSONS, D. F., W. D. BONNER, JR., AND J. G. VERBOON. "Electron Microscopy of Isolated Plant Mitochondria and Plastids Using Both the Thin-Section and Negative-Staining Techniques." *Canadian Journal of Botany,* Vol. 43, p. 647.

CULTURAL AND PHYSIOLOGICAL ASPECTS
OF THE LICHEN SYMBIOSIS

9

Vernon Ahmadjian

Department of Biology
Clark University

Lichens are unusual associations. They are, on the one hand, distinct morphological entities, easily recognized and classified in separate taxonomic groups. Yet when their two individual components, fungus and alga, are separated in laboratory cultures, each has its own distinctive characteristics and bears little resemblance to the composite plant. In effect, when we consider one lichen we seem to be dealing with three plants—a fungus, an alga, and the lichen. Some investigators have even proposed separate names for all three units. Small wonder, then, that when Simon Schwendener stated in 1867 that a lichen was the product of a union between two organisms, a storm of controversy arose. Botanists who were accustomed to regarding lichens as separate groups of plants could not accept this radical new idea, this romance of lichenology as the Rev. James M. Crombie (1874) phrased it. It was difficult to conceive that lichens were merely different forms of or closely related to existing organisms. As Crombie in 1884 stated, "Lichens therefore are Lichens and nothing else—neither Fungi nor Algae, nor any intermixture of these." Although Schwendener's theory was a difficult one to accept, numerous investigations established that there were indeed two organisms and that a genetic independence did exist between them. The question now raised so frequently is How does one define a lichen association?

A mixture of alga and fungus is not a lichen. If a mushroom is covered with green algae, it is not considered a lichen, even though its individual hyphae may be intimately associated with the algal cells, and some sort of mutualistic relationship can be demonstrated. In this article, the term "symbiosis" is used in its original meaning—that is, a close association of dissimilar organisms. Mutualism is a type of symbiosis where, as with lichens, both organisms benefit from the association. A lichen represents not only a physiological interplay between fungus and alga, but the association results also in an entirely new morphological entity in which the fungus and sometimes the alga become modified in form and lose their free-living identities.

In view of the acceptance of the dual nature of lichens, the problem arises about whether there could be a more natural reclassification of these organisms in the taxonomic framework of the plant kingdom. Most investigators at present favor classifying lichens among fungi, since the fungal component is in most instances the dominant partner. The fungus determines what shape a lichen body or thallus assumes and also forms fruiting structures comparable to those of other free-living fungi. Because fruiting structures are important criteria for taxonomic identification, it is possible to relate lichens to existing groups of fungi. For this reason, the name of a lichen refers only to its fungal component even when the fungus is grown separately in laboratory culture. We might, therefore, consider lichens as various types of fungi that have entered into lichenized associations with algae. The terms "mycobiont" and "phycobiont" have been proposed to designate fungal and algal components, respectively, of lichens.

Experimental studies of lichens have been conducted in two ways. One method has been to study the whole plant, another way to study the isolated components under cultural conditions. Both methods are necessary for the fullest understanding of the association, and whichever is chosen depends on the type of information an investigator wishes to determine. Problems of nutrition—such as carbon, nitrogen, and vitamin requirements—or genetic and sexual investigations can best be conducted with the isolated components. Since the organisms are in pure (=axenic) culture, experiments can be extended over long periods, allowing for a more critical analysis of results. Although metabolic studies of photosynthesis and respiration can be carried out using both approaches, information obtained from the separate symbionts must be extended with some degree of caution to the naturally occurring composite plant. Conditions of culture are far different from the varied and varying ones that a lichen encounters in its natural habitat. Unfortunately, it is not possible to grow or even to maintain a lichen in pure culture for any length of time. First, it is difficult to rid a thallus of epiphytic organisms such as bacteria, fungi, and algae. Second, the association is a very labile one and tends to break down under the usual conditions of laboratory culture. It is possible, however, to maintain a lichen under laboratory conditions for short periods, allowing for studies such as water uptake, absorption of nutrients, and transport of radioactive compounds from one part of the thallus to another. With some lichens, especially species of *Cladonia,* limited developmental studies can be made in the laboratory. When small discs are cut from a thallus and placed onto illuminated filter paper strips kept moist with a mineral solution, within two or three days, lichen stalks (=podetia) and fruits will appear on a small percentage of the discs. Formation of these structures shows a seasonal influence, the greatest number being produced by discs obtained from lichens collected in summer and late fall. A recent breakthrough in the problem of the artificial re-establishment of a lichen (Ahmadjian, 1966b) allows for developmental studies of a lichen's vegetative as well as fruiting structures in pure culture (Fig. 9–1).

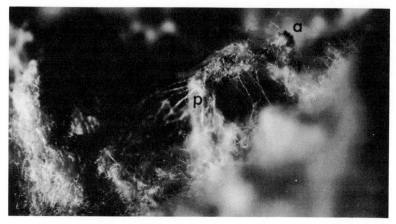

FIG. 9–1. Fruiting structure formed by the lichen fungus *Cladonia cristatella* in artificial culture. The curvature of the podetium (p) was the result of a phototropic response, probably mediated by the red pigment produced by the young apothecia (a). × 25. [Photograph by A. A. Blaker.]

ISOLATION AND CULTURE OF THE ALGAL COMPONENT

Thirty-two genera of algae, twenty green, eleven blue-green, and one yellow-green, have been reported as being members of lichen associations (Ahmadjian, 1958), and undoubtedly there are more. Isolation of algae from lichens can be accomplished by means of several techniques. The simplest method is to keep a thallus fragment into antiseptic solutions such as Clorox for varying periods some type of illumination. A northerly exposed window will suffice. After several weeks, outgrowths of the algal component should be visible and can be transferred to a mineral agar medium. It must be remembered that a lichen thallus has many epiphytic organisms, including different types of algae, which generally have faster rates of growth than the lichen symbionts. It is almost a certainty that under the sustained conditions of moisture experienced in a damp chamber, a number of epiphytes will form colonies on the thallus—some, like certain fungi, so rapidly, that the entire lichen specimen may be overgrown in a short time. For this reason, cells of any alga that develops on the thallus must be compared microscopically with those of the algal partner to insure that the true phycobiont has been isolated. Placing a lichen for fifteen to twenty minutes under running, cold tap water will reduce the number of epiphytes. Some investigators have soaked lichens in 2M KCl or $MgSO_4$ solutions in attempts to plasmolyze epiphytic forms. Dipping a thallus fragment into antiseptic solutions such as Clorox for varying periods has also been effective. Another method of isolation is to fragment a thallus in a blender and spread some of the resulting suspension over the surface of an agar medium that contains mineral salts. The phycobiont will develop more rapidly with this method, since fragmentation results in freeing many algal cells from the confinement caused by fungal hyphae. With green phycobionts, pure cultures can be achieved by transferring to an organic nutrient agar medium those colonies that appear to be free from foreign organisms. Blue-green algae invariably have within their cellular gelatinous sheaths bacteria that frustrate any pure culture attempts. However, by means of antibiotics and ultraviolet radiation it is possible to destroy the sheath bacteria without damaging algal cells.

The best but, unfortunately, most time-consuming method of phycobiont isolation is by means of a micropipette drawn from a glass tube of narrow (3–4 mm) diameter. The micropipette technique (Pringsheim, 1949), once mastered, has several advantages. Single cells can be isolated that form colonies of a single genetic type, and by selecting cells that have pieces of adhering fungal hyphae, one is certain that the alga isolated is the lichen phycobiont. In this general procedure, small portions of a recently collected and washed thallus are crushed lightly between two glass surfaces until a green suspension results. A drop of this suspension examined with a microscope will show many single algal cells, a number of them with bits of the fungus still attached. Cells of this type that appear to be in good condition are then transferred with a micropipette through a series of five to six drops of water on a glass slide. All materials, of course, are sterilized before use. In this manner, cells are removed from contaminant organisms and can be transferred to tubes of organic nutrient agar. Before the last two transfers, the micropipette tip can be sterilized by briefly holding it in a jet of steam generated from distilled water contained in an Erlenmeyer flask that has a cork stopper with a bent glass tube tapered at one end. Cultures can be kept either in light or dark. Trebouxiae will show some growth in a temperature range of 1–27°C, but temperatures of 18–20°C support the best development of most strains. The pH range is also a wide one, from 4.0–9.1, the optima of most somewhere near 7.0. Colonies will be barely visible to the naked eye between two to six weeks after isolation. With lichens that have algal symbionts normally filamentous in a free-living condition—such as, *Trentepohlia*, *Nostoc*, and *Scytonema*—the same technique can be used, but fragments of a thallus are first kept in an illuminated mineral solution for several months until the phycobiont forms filaments that grow out of the thallus.

The majority of lichens in temperate zones contain as phycobionts various strains of the genus *Trebouxia*—a unicellular, green algal genus belonging to the order Chlorococcales. These lichen algae have been the ones most studied for cultural behavior. Trebouxiae are characterized by spherical or ellipsoidal cells with a large, centrally located chromatophore that has a single pyrenoid. A large nucleus with a prominent nucleolus is located near the outer margin of the cell, usually between two lobes of the chromatophore. Margins of the chromatophore may be deeply incised, with branches extending out to the cell wall, or comparatively smooth, the chromatophore lying some distance from the cell wall. Division of a cell is by means of a successive bipartition of the protoplast, which can result in over 200 small pieces of the chromatophore, each with accompanying nucleus and small amount of cytoplasm, within the original mother cell wall. At this point, environmental conditions determine the nature of the future product. With an adequate amount of moisture, nutrient materials, and uncrowded conditions, each protoplast fragment will develop into a motile spore or zoospore. If conditions are dry or nutrient materials are low, a cell wall is formed by each of the protoplast segments, which are then called aplanospores (Fig. 9–2). An aplanospore is a miniature form of the mother cell. Both types of spores are released by a rupture of the mother cell wall. Zoospores swim about

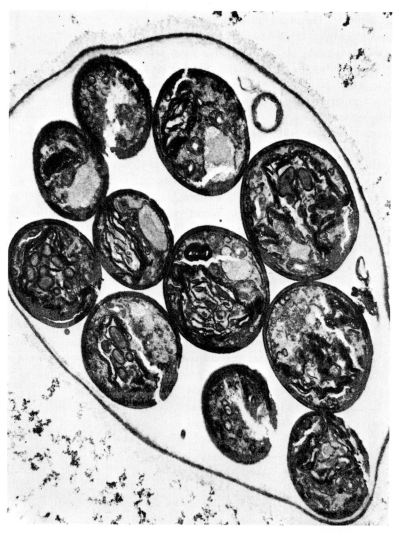

FIG. 9–2. Aplanospores of a *Trebouxia* phycobiont (from the lichen *Parmelia caperata*) grown in culture. Cell wall and gelatinous sheath of parent cell still enclose the spores. × 6,400. [Photograph by G. Chapman.]

for awhile but eventually come to rest, withdraw their flagella into the cytoplasm, assume a rounded form, develop a cell wall about the unit membrane, and become transformed into an aplanospore that, after a week or more, attains the size of the parent cell. Frequently, there are found irregularly shaped motile forms that represent an incomplete cleavage of parts of the protoplast. Sometimes one can observe the fusion of two motile bodies (gametes), but beyond this observance and the fact that the resulting zygote increases to a size of other cells and then divides by successive bipartition, little is known of the sexual processes of these algae.

There are several differences between the cultural as opposed to natural or lichenized characteristics of these algae. In a lichen, algal cells are half the size they are in culture, they form far fewer aplanospores, and they do not produce zoospores—at least, no one has observed the presence of zoospores within a lichen thallus. Motile spores probably fail to form because of frequent dry periods and conditions of low nutrient supply which a lichen is subjected to in its natural habitat. A few algae in culture produce a gelatinous sheath not found when they are part of the lichen. When lichen algae are cultured, there are also physiological changes, such as decreased permeability and increased sensitivity to high temperatures.

Colonies of Trebouxiae on nutrient agar media are compact, elevated, and of various shapes and consistencies—traits that aid in identifying different strains.

Some years ago it was thought that each lichen had its own specific algal partner and that spores from the lichen fruits could not produce a composite plant until the fungal component which they gave rise to somehow encountered an algal type identical to that of the parent lichen. If we assume a conservative estimate of 15,000 different lichens, this would necessitate an equal number of different algae. The idea has been proved false by investigations that have discovered in widely differing types of lichens morphologically identical algae, which in some cases also had physiological attributes in common. Moreover, numerous lichens with green phycobionts also form smaller, secondary associations (cephalodia) on the same thalli with blue-green algae. A few lichens have two distinct algal layers, one green and the other blue-green. Some variation exists even among the phycobiont of a single thallus. Cells may differ in physiology and also in morphology, probably due in part to mutations and incorporation by the growing lichen of fragments of other lichens. There is no evidence against the possibility of the presence of different algal types within one thallus or a group of individuals belonging to one species of lichens. Predominance of one particular alga in a thallus or group of individuals is a reflection of the asexual type of reproduction that the phycobiont is limited to within a thallus and the fact that lichens are dispersed mainly by means of fragmentation mechanisms. It is doubtful whether lichen fungi are specifically adapted to any alga. There is evidence to show that these fungi will form preliminary associations with all types of algae. Further development depends on whether an alga can survive the conditions imposed upon it by the fungus—that is, the type of penetration that the fungus makes on the alga (Fig. 9–3), amount of nutrient material

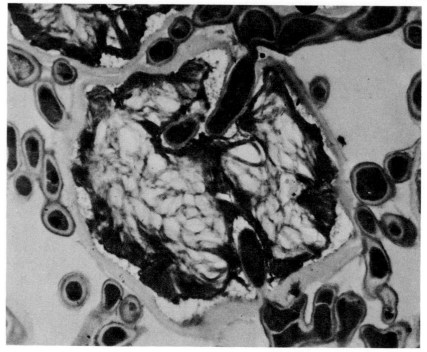

FIG. 9–3. *Maronella laricina*. Phycobiont cell (*Myrmecia pyriformis*) with three intracellular haustoria. Section of natural lichen. × 8,000. [Photograph by R. F. Nunnemacher.]

taken from the algal cells, and the amount of shading caused by fungal filaments. In many cases, it has been possible to relate a lichen alga with a free-living species, the two forms usually being found in the same area but in different microclimates. The lichenized form is better able to withstand drier habitats than its free-living counterpart. One of the most puzzling situations is the fact that Trebouxiae, the most common of phycobionts, are not found in abundance in free-living conditions. Two free-living *Trebouxia* strains have been reported, but these may have originated from small lichen fragments in which the fungal component had disintegrated. The same characteristics—that is, slow rate of growth, low optimum light intensity, and preference for organic nitrogen sources —that make these algae successful in lichenized associations apparently place them at a disadvantage in the competition found in free-living conditions.

Although information does exist on the basic nutritional requirements and physiological behavior of a few phycobionts (Ahmadjian, 1962b), there is need for similar investigations of other types of lichen algae. To provide information necessary for a clearer understanding of the lichen symbiosis, a variety of experiments could be designed to study the effect of pigments excreted by mycobionts on the photosynthetic rates of their algal partners and resistance of the separated algae to environmental extremes.

ISOLATION AND CULTURE OF THE FUNGAL COMPONENT

Four tropical lichens have been reported to be composed of members of the fungal class Basidiomycetes and blue-green algae; there are also a number of lichens with fungal partners that do not form fruiting bodies (Imperfect lichens). But all other known lichens are composed of members of the fungal class Ascomycetes and either green or blue-green algae. Our discussion will be limited to Ascomycetous lichens.

Isolation of mycobionts is achieved best by means of the fruiting structures found so commonly and in many instances so abundantly on lichen thalli. The fruits, products of the fungus alone, are typical of those produced by other free-living ascomycetes; the fruits are of two main types. One type is of a saucer, disc, or button shape and is found on the thallus surface or on a stalklike extension of it; the other type is produced within the thallus and is flask-shaped with a necklike projection that forms an opening at the surface of the thallus. Each fruit contains many sacs (asci), each of which generally contains eight spores (ascospores).

Freshly collected lichens are soaked in running tap water for fifteen to twenty minutes. Fruiting bodies are then removed from the thallus, touched to absorbent tissue to remove excess water, and fixed by means of vaseline to an upper half of a petri dish. Plastic dishes are preferred to glass because of their ease of handling and better visibility. The upper half of the dish is then placed over the lower half, which may contain either agar (2 percent) alone or agar with mineral or soil-extract additives. It is possible to use an organic nutrient agar, but this would support a more rapid growth of any contaminant organisms that may be present, and it is no more effective than the other media in influencing spore germination. Spore discharge is variable. Some lichens, such as species of *Cladonia,* discharge spores within minutes after the washed fruits are fixed to the plates; others take hours, and a few may take a day or more. Spores are discharged forceably, because of the pressure and subsequent rupture of asci caused by the slow drying of a fruiting body. Discharged spores are generally free from contaminant organisms and can reach heights of .1– 3 cm. In a very few lichens, cells of the phycobiont grow inside the fruits and are carried along with the spores. Spores emerge either singly or in packets along with, in some forms, numerous droplets of ascus sap. Once spore germination has occurred— almost always within two to three days—small pieces of the agar with one or several spores are cut out with a sterilized implement and transferred to tubes of nutrient agar. The germination of spores can be followed, without opening the dish, by placing the inverted dish on the microscope stage and observing with low magnification. Cultures are maintained best at 18–21 °C, but the temperature range at which growth will occur is from 1–28 °C. The optimal pH range is from 4.5–7.4. There is no evidence to show that light in the visible range has any influence on the growth of these fungi.

The fruits of lichens are perennial, but the amount of spore discharge is variable, being highest in early spring and fall. From a randomly collected group of lichens, about 50 percent will discharge spores (much less if collections are made directly after a heavy rainfall), and of these lichens, the spores of half the number of forms will germinate. In some cases, spores will germinate but further growth does not occur. The reasons why spores of many lichens fail to germinate or to grow further, at least in culture, are not known, and very few experiments have been conducted to determine the causes for such failures.

Mycobionts can be isolated also by means of hyphal fragments or small bits of the thallus. For example, with large, leafy lichens, the upper layer can be cut away to reveal a white medulla composed solely of fungal filaments. Using a pair of fine forceps and a dissecting microscope, a few fungal strands can be teased out and transferred to nutrient agar tubes. Contamination is a serious problem with this technique, and many times one cannot be sure whether the isolated fungus represents the true mycobiont or a contaminant form growing on or even within the thallus.

Growth of lichen fungi in culture is extremely variable but, in general, slow when compared to other free-living molds. It may take several months before a colony on agar achieves a size of a few millimeters in diameter, but this may be a reflection of the particular cultural conditions under which the fungus was grown. Growth depends upon a number of factors, such as temperature, pH, carbon, and nitrogen sources; the proper combination of these factors that will support optimal growth for a particular fungus varies considerably. A number of mycobionts—for example, species of *Cladonia*, *Acarospora*, and *Sarcogyne*— have growth rates comparable to or approaching those of some free-living forms, and they can be used readily for investigations of nutritional requirements.

Lichen fungi in culture have certain distinguishing characteristics. They have compact and elevated colonies, usually of a hard or rubbery consistency (Fig. 9–4). A few produce asexual spores such as conidia, which are of some assistance in relating these fungi to free-living forms in order to discover some of the originations of lichens, but most fungi consist wholly of vegetative mycelium. There may be a few superficial resemblances to the composite plant, but this is not the usual case.

The problem of sexuality in lichen fungi is one of the most challenging in lichenology. Because of the variability among fungal cultures derived from single ascospores from one lichen, it is reasonable to assume that sexual mechanisms

FIG. 9–4. Three-month-old colony of the mycobiont *Stereocaulon dactylophyllum* growing on a malt extract–yeast extract agar medium. Colony measures 1.1 cm in diameter and is .5 cm high.

that include fusion of heterogeneous nuclei do exist among lichens. Most lichen thalli contain numerous small, dark, flask-shaped bodies (pycnidia) that produce innumerable small sporelike bodies (pycniospores). Pycnidia and pycniospores are excreted in stringlike gelatinous masses. As in other ascomycetous fungi, it seems likely that pycnidia serve as male gametes. These male gametes are washed onto specialized filaments, either on the same or a different thallus. Each of these filaments contains a female nucleus. This process of fertilization has been seen in naturally occurring lichens by many investigators—at least to the point where male gametes fuse to a part of the female filament.

Another problem with mycobionts in culture is their failure to form the same chemical compounds, so-called "lichen acids," which they synthesize so abundantly when in lichenized associations. Separated lichen fungi produce many different types of chemical substances, such as pigments, that color the colonies or are excreted into the medium, or large quantities of viscous material that accumulates in liquid media or in large drops on a colony. Also, lichen fungi produce various types of crystals that encrust the fungal filaments and often form large masses on the colonies and surrounding agar. Except for two or three of the fungal products, none of the substances produced by these organisms in culture is identical to what they form under natural conditions in association with algae. Some of the compounds, produced in culture by fungi are simpler moieties of lichen acids and cannot be synthesized to the final form without a collaborative effort of the algal partners, perhaps by means of enzymes to couple the simpler moieties and form the final products. Many lichen compounds have antibiotic and other biological activities. In fact, several European countries sell antibiotics made from two lichen compounds. Obviously, the limiting factor in any widespread usage or testing of these substances is the amount of lichen material available in nature. If the fungi alone could manufacture these products, a continuous supply could be obtained, even of those types formed by small, inconspicuous crustose lichens.

Information exists on the basic nutritional requirements of a few mycobionts (Quispel, 1959; Smith, 1962, 1963)—that is, their carbon and nitrogen preferences and deficiencies for vitamins such as biotin and thiamine. But there is a need for more information on the basic nutritional requirements from other types of lichen fungi. Also, more studies of the genetic and sexual mechanisms of these fungi need to be conducted.

RE-SYNTHESIS AND PHYSIOLOGY OF THE LICHEN ASSOCIATION

Many attempts have been made to re-establish a lichen association beginning with isolated fungal and algal components. Although most experiments were unsuccessful or achieved only preliminary stages, they did illustrate conditions that were necessary for such syntheses. The association will form only on a nutrient deficient medium—one that will not support growth of either component for any length of time. If both partners are cultured on an organic nutrient agar, each grows independently of the other, resulting in an intermixture. Even on an illuminated mineral medium, the alga develops much more than the fungus and a union is not formed. A lichen association reflects a balanced growth between fungus and alga. Conditions such as excess nutrient, light, or moisture tend to cause an imbalance of growth and prevent a union or even break down an established association. This can be tested by subjecting freshly collected lichen thalli, or small fragments of them, to these conditions and noting a gradual dissolution of the symbiosis.

A partially successful case of lichen synthesis was accomplished (Ahmadjian, 1962a, 1963) with the lichen *Acarospora fuscata,* a brown, crustose form commonly found on rocks in temperate areas. The mycobiont was grown first for one week in a vitamin-free, mannitol, asparagine liquid medium (Lilly and Barnett, 1951, p. 427), then filtered and washed with distilled water and fragmented in a sterile blender for about fifteen seconds. The phycobiont was taken from tubes of Bristol's mineral agar medium and mixed briefly, by means of the blender, with the fungus. Equal amounts of the resulting suspension, which contained both algal cells and fungal filaments, were then transferred to a series of flasks that contained the following media: A highly purified agar (Difco 0560-02), agar with mineral salts, and agar with mineral salts and dextrose. Flasks were kept at various levels of light intensity that ranged from 30 to 400 footcandles. The last two media supported independent growth of one or both components and clearly were not favorable for lichen synthesis. On the first medium, development of the association could be followed, beginning with an encirclement of algal cells by fungal filaments (Fig. 9–5) and subsequent formation by the mycobiont of a tissue-like pseudoparenchyma around the algal cells (Fig. 9–6). This tissue, identical to that found in natural forms, was formed after about thirty days in culture. The cultures were kept for more

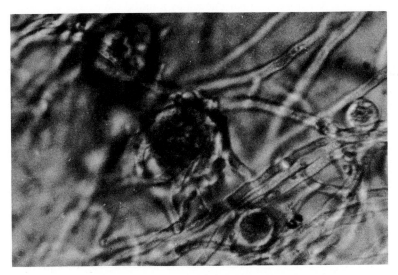

FIG. 9–5. Top view of an algal cell enveloped by fungal filaments. This is the beginning stage of lichen synthesis which can be accomplished in the laboratory. Lichen: *Acarospora fuscata.* × 1,400.

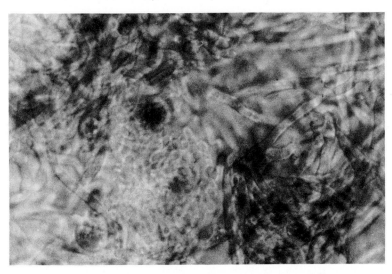

FIG. 9–6. Intermediate stage of a lichen synthesis. Fungal filaments have subdivided into many small cells which form a compact, protective tissue (pseudoparenchyma) around the algal cells. Lichen: *Acarospora fuscata.* × 1,400.

than one year, and the continued healthy appearance of algal cells enclosed in this tissue contrasted sharply with the dead and disintegrated algal cells in the same flask which were not surrounded by a fungal tissue. The pseudoparenchyma with its enclosed algal cells not only looked like but also behaved like a lichenized unit. Moreover, after five months, cells of the mycobiont that made up the pseudoparenchyma produced a pigment that the fungus in culture formed only on a medium that contained an excess of organic supplements. Filaments in the same flask that were not in contact with algae did not produce a pigment. This is indirect evidence to support the logical assumption of a transfer of materials between the two partners in an association. Also, in flasks closest to the light source, the pseudoparenchyma protected the algal cells from the lethal effects of the higher light intensities. The pseudoparenchyma units developed only to small, poorly organized, juvenile thalli. It was apparent that further development would require additional conditions. Possibly the sustained moisture of the agar prevented formation of a mature thallus.

In a second set of experiments, a mixture of both components was grown on organic nutrient agar for several months, and then portions of the growth were scraped from the agar, kept in an illuminated mineral medium for several weeks, and placed on small, sterilized rock fragments from which colonies of *Acarospora fuscata* were removed. Cultures were subjected to alternate wetting and drying, both by varying the humidity of the incubator and flooding and drying the cultures directly with distilled water. Under these conditions, lichenization proceeded rapidly, and the mixture after several months assumed the shape of a small thallus, which microscopically and macroscopically resembled the naturally occurring lichen. A light brown pigment colored only parts of the thallus and probably would have formed more uniformly and fully in response to higher temperatures and light intensities. In nature, this lichen grows on rocks whose surface temperature may rise above 38°C and is subjected to light intensities of 10,000 to 12,000 footcandles for several hours on bright, sunny days. It is evident, therefore, that conditions for a successful synthesis include not only a nutrient-poor substrate but also alternate wetting and drying of cultures and perhaps fluctuation of other factors, such as temperature and light intensity. Fruiting structures were not formed by any of the cultures.

A third set of experiments (Ahmadjian, 1966b) was conducted with the lichen *Cladonia cristatella*. Spores from the lichen's fruits were allowed to discharge onto a nutritive agar medium which contained a fragment of rotted wood (e.g., apple, maple), a favorable substrate for this lichen under natural conditions. After the spores had germinated, a suspension of the algal symbiont was added to the culture flasks. Incubation was at 20°C under constant illumination (100 footcandles). Within a few weeks, the alga formed a continous cover over the agar surface and parts of the wood. After a few months, numerous colonies of the mycobiont grew up through the algal cover. As the cultures slowly dried, the fungi formed the reproductive structures—that is, pycnidia and young fruits borne on small stalks (Fig. 9–1). The immature fruits contained female reproductive filaments but no asci. Although the number of reproductive structures was greatest in flasks that contained the algal symbiont and a wood fragment, both fruits and pycnidia were produced by the mycobiont in the absence of the alga and the wood. The stimulus for the formation of the reproductive structures was slow drying. Mycobionts which had been in culture for several years did not form reproductive structures under similar experimental conditions. They did, however, form the vegetative lichen structures in cultures with the algal partner.

The following conclusions, based on the above described experiments, have been reached with regard to the lichen synthesis problem. (1) The algal symbiont is not a necessary prerequisite to the fruiting of the lichen fungus in culture. (2) The fungal partner in culture gradually loses its ability to fruit but can still form lichenized unions with algae. (3) Spores of a lichen are capable of re-establishing the lichenized states in culture and probably also in natural conditions. (4) The most important stimuli for the establishment of lichen associations are nutrient-poor conditions and drying.

The physiological relationships of lichen symbioses have been the subject of much speculation, largely because of the difficulties involved in experimenting with these organisms. Now, however, with the availability of radioactive tracers and autoradiographic techniques, which only recently have been applied to problems in lichenology, it is possible to substitute experimentation for speculation. One investigator (Smith, 1961; Smith and Drew, 1965) traced the movement of organic compounds from alga to fungus in the lichen *Peltigera polydactyla*, using sodium bicarbonate ($NaHCO_3$) labeled with C^{14}. Discs were cut from the lichen thallus and floated on an aqueous solution of the labeled compound. Discs were illuminated for eight hours and then kept in darkness for seven hours. Periodically, discs were removed and after the algal and fungal layers were separated by dissection, the amount of C^{14} present in each of the layers was then determined by scintillation counting. Results showed that C^{14}-labeled organic compounds (mostly the sugar alcohol mannitol) appeared first in the algal layer and later were found in the fungal layer. The artificial synthesis of lichen tissue in culture offers an excellent opportunity for use of autoradiographic techniques.

Many questions remain unanswered in our understanding of the physiological relationships of a lichen association. From mostly indirect evidence we can formulate a crude picture of the symbiosis. The alga synthesizes an excess of organic materials and thereby supports not only itself but also the mycobiont which in turn provides the alga with water as well as minerals and provides some protection from dessication and high light intensities and temperatures. The finding that many lichen fungi are unable to synthesize needed vitamins such as thiamine and biotin suggests that they obtain these items from their phycobionts, a possibility supported by the finding that some lichen algae excrete vitamins, including thiamine and biotin. It is not known to what extent a lichen obtains organic and inorganic materials from the substrate on which it grows or from airborne contamination, but it is obvious that the amount obtained is, in most cases, insufficient to sustain prolonged independent growth of either component since this would tend to dissolve the union. One important aspect of the symbiosis that should be investigated is whether the flow of materials between the symbionts occurs at a uniform rate throughout the growth season or whether the fungus, through chemical intermediates, has a direct influence on the metabolic activities of the alga. Several of the fungal processes such as growth and fruit formation are more prevalent during certain times of the year than others. Since these processes require increased supply of food materials, the fungus could at these times stimulate the metabolic rate of the alga and thereby increase the flow of organic materials.

The many unexplored facets of a lichen symbiosis offer to the patient and imaginative investigator a challenging area for research.

GUIDE TO THE LITERATURE

Recent reviews on lichens include several on the biology of lichen symbioses by Quispel (1959), Smith (1962, 1963), Schaede (1962), Steiner (1964), Haynes (1964), and Ahmadjian (1965, 1966a), one on lichen anatomy and morphology by Ozenda (1963), reviews on lichen taxonomy by Weber (1962) and Thomson (1963), on lichen chemistry by Shibata (1958, 1963), and lichen ecology by Barkman (1958). Llano (1944, 1951) has published detailed reviews on the economic uses of lichens. General reviews have been written by Hale (1961) and Des Abbayes (1951). Lists of recent publications on all aspects of lichenology are published by Culberson in each issue of *The Bryologist* which is a quarterly journal of the American Bryological Society.

REFERENCES

AHMADJIAN, V. "A Guide for the Identification of Algae Occurring as Lichen Symbionts." *Botaniska Notiser*, Vol. 111 (1958), pp. 632–644.
———. "Experimental Observations on the Algal Genus *Trebouxia* de Puymaly." *Svensk Botanisk Tidskrift*, Vol. 53 (1959), pp. 71–80.
———. "Studies on Lichenized Fungi." *The Bryologist*, Vol. 64 (1961), pp. 168–179.
———. "Investigations on Lichen Synthesis." *American Journal of Botany*, Vol. 49 (1962a), pp. 227–283.
———. "Lichens." *Physiology and Biochemistry of Algae*. New York: Academic Press, Inc., 1962b. pp. 817–822.
———. "The Fungi of Lichens." *Scientific American*, Vol. 208 (1963), pp. 122–132.
———. "Lichens." *Annual Review of Microbiology*. Vol. 19 (1965), pp. 1–20.
———. "Lichens." *Symbosis: Its Physical and Biochemical Significance*. New York: Academic Press, Inc., 1966a. pp. 35–97. Vol. 1.
———. "Artificial Reestablishment of the Lichen *Cladonia cristatella*." *Science*, Vol. 151 (1966b), pp. 199–201.
BARKMAN, J. J. *Phytosociology and Ecology of Cryptogamic Epiphytes*. Assen, Netherlands: Van Gorcum, 1958. 628 pp.
CROMBIE, J. M. "On the Lichen-Gonidia Question." *Popular Science Review*, Vol. 13 (1874), pp. 260–277.

————. "On the Algo-lichen Hypothesis." *Journal of the Linnean Society* (Botany), Vol. 21 (1884), pp. 259–283.

DES ABBAYES, H. *Traité de Lichénologie*. Paris: Lechevalier, 1951. 217 pp.

HALE, M. E. *Lichen Handbook*. Washington, D.C.: Smithsonian Institution Publication No. 4434, 1961. 178 pp.

HAYNES, F. N. "Lichens." *Viewpoints in Biology*. London: Butterworths, 1964. pp. 64–115. Vol. 3.

LAMB, I. M. "Lichens." *Scientific American*, Vol. 201 (1959), pp. 144–156.

LILLY, V. G., AND H. L. BARNETT. *Physiology of the Fungi*. New York: McGraw-Hill Book Co., Inc., 1951. 464 pp.

LLANO, G. A. "Lichens: Their Biological and Economic Significance." *Botanical Review*, Vol. 10 (1944), pp. 1–65.

————. "Economic Uses of Lichens." Washington, D.C.: Smithsonian Institution Report (1950), 1951. pp. 385–422.

OZENDA, P. "Lichens." *Handbuch der Pflanzenanatomie*, Vol. 6 (1963), pp. 1–199.

PRINGSHEIM, E. G. *Pure Cultures of Algae*. New York: Cambridge University Press, 1949. 119 pp.

QUISPEL, A. "Lichens." *Handbuch der Pflanzenphysiologie*, Vol. 11 (1955), pp. 577–604.

SCHAEDE, R. (3rd ed. by F. H. Meyer.) "Die Flechten." *Die Pflanzlichen Symbiosen*. Stuttgart: Fischer, 1962. pp. 90–125.

SCHWENDENER, S. In "Protokoll der botanischen Sektion." *Verhandlungen der Schweizerischen Naturforschenden Gesellschaft*, Vol. 51 (1867), pp. 88–91.

SHIBATA, S. "Especial Compounds of Lichens." *Handbuch der Pflanzenphysiologie*, Vol. 10 (1958), pp. 560–623.

————. "Lichen Substances." *Modern Methods of Plant Analysis*, Vol. 6 (1963), pp. 155–193.

SMITH, D. C. "The Physiology of *Peltigera polydactyla* (Neck.) Hoffm." *The Lichenologist*, Vol. 1 (1961), pp. 209–226.

————. "The Biology of Lichen Thalli." *Biological Reviews*, Vol. 37 (1962), pp. 537–570.

————. "Experimental Studies of Lichen Physiology." *Symposia of the Society for General Microbiology*, Vol. 13 (1963), pp. 31–50.

————, AND E. A. DREW. "Studies in the Physiology of Lichens: V, Translocation from the Algal Layer to the Medulla in *Peltigera polydactyla*." *New Phytologist*, Vol. 64 (1965), pp. 195–200.

STEINER, M. "Wachstums- und Entwicklungs-physiologie der Flechten." *Handbuch der Pflanzenphysiologie*, Vol. 15, Part 1 (1964), pp. 758–801.

THOMSON, J. W. "Modern Species Concepts: Lichens." *The Bryologist*, Vol. 66 (1963), pp. 94–100.

WEBER, W. A. "Environmental Modification and the Taxonomy of the Crustose Lichens." *Svensk Botanisk Tidskrift*, Vol. 56 (1962), pp. 293–333.

MODERN RESEARCH ON EVOLUTION IN THE FERNS

10

W. H. Wagner, Jr.

Department of Botany
The University of Michigan

The period 1940 to 1960 saw a major breakthrough in our understandings of DNA and molecular biology. The shift of emphasis was toward analysis rather than synthesis, and the biologists of whole organisms were eclipsed. Now once again the pendulum is swinging. During the past several years, scientists have begun to turn again to problems at the organismal level. Complex questions of ontogeny, evolution, and ecology must be addressed by new approaches. One of the major stimuli has come from the intrusion of modern statistical and electronic computer methods into biology. The correlation of multiple data is of primary interest. Modern ideas about ecology, evolution, and the dynamics of populations are more and more influencing our ideas of taxonomy and classification. The following devices, among others, are making it possible to obtain valuable data quickly and efficiently: cytogenetic techniques of forming interspecific and intergeneric hybrids and of determining chromosome characters by squashing techniques; anatomical methods of clearing whole plant organs with sodium hydroxide and studying the interrelationships of parts three-dimensionally, and chemical procedures of making chromatograms to analyze chemical components. The re-awakening of questions concerning the nature of organisms is reflected in the upsurge in programs at various universities in "Biosystematics," "Population Biology," and "Evolutionary Biology."

The ferns or Filicineae, which I am going to use, have long been popular materials for illustrating research on evolution in higher plants. During the past fifteen years we have seen an especially active interest. The ferns have a long and distinguished fossil history that runs back at least to the Carboniferous, some 300 million years ago. Some of the families that existed then—the Osmundaceae, Schizaeaceae, and Gleicheniaceae—still grow on the earth today. However, the fossils have been of little help in working out their evolutionary relationships thus far. Fortunately the living diversity of ferns, including very

164

primitive types and very specialized ones, is very extensive. There are some nine to ten thousand species, their leaves varying from one-quarter of an inch in length to one hundred feet, their habits from mosslike plants to tall, columnar trees, and all sorts of reproductive structures and life cycles. By studying this great range of diversity we can find very definite patterns and trace out pathways of evolutionary relationships with considerable probability.

The fern plant itself is "made to order" for researchers and teachers. It is simple in construction—leaf, stem, and root. The sexual plant or gametophyte stage is easy to culture in quantity, and usually does not require complicated techniques to study. The sporophyte plant grows readily in glass-enclosed terraria or greenhouses—so long as the atmosphere is humid and they are not watered too violently. The gametophytes or prothallia germinate readily from spores on water with minerals, on damp soil, chips of flower pots, or nutrient agar. Dried specimens make beautiful classroom demonstrations that are fairly unique among vascular plant specimens since they are not usually attacked by museum pests.

THE PATTERNS OF EVOLUTION

The ferns illustrate well the basic patterns of evolution, as well as some of the important processes. By patterns of evolution we shall mean the amount, directions, and sequences of biological changes that our knowledge permits us to deduce. Probably the most important and basic pattern of all is *divergence*— the tendency of populations, once separated by breeding barriers on or near the species level, to become more and more different as evolution proceeds. It would be ideal if all evolution occurred in different directions—that is, involved different changes. But this is not the case always. Probably the most serious problem we have is *parallelism*, the tendency of separate evolutionary lines to produce similar characteristics. Long ago, the British botanist F. A. Bower pointed out the great extent of parallel evolution in the ferns. In more recent times a large number of new examples have come to light. The question is simply this: If we have two kinds of ferns, are the similarities between them the result of common ancestry or have these similarities actually arisen separately, along different lines? Often whole series of similarities have arisen independently in different lines, and it requires very careful correlations to recognize them. In Fig. 10–1A,B is illustrated a simple case involving vegetative reproduction and modification of the leaf. *Polystichum rhizophyllum* of the Caribbean region has the same attenuate, threadlike leaf tip that produces a new plant as *Asplenium pinnatifidum* of eastern North America, yet the plants belong to different families or subfamilies of ferns and have evidently produced this modification separately. Another example (Fig. 10–1C) illustrates *Aspleniopsis decipiens* of New Caledonia, which so resembles certain species of *Asplenium* (Fig. 10–1D) that a careless identifier would put it in the wrong family. In Fig. 10–2B is shown *Drymotaenium miyoshianum* of Japan (Polypodiaceae), which is extraordinarily

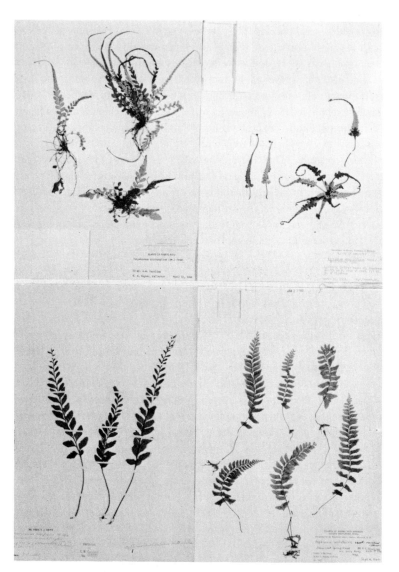

FIG. 10–1. Top: Parallel evolution of leaf and propagation method—
(A) *Polystichum rhizophyllum* (Aspidiaceae) vs. (B) *Asplenium
pinnatifidum* (Aspleniaceae). Bottom: Leaf and sorus shape—
(C) *Aspleniopsis decipiens* (Pteridaceae) vs. (D) *Asplenium uni-
laterale* (Aspleniaceae).

similar to species of *Vittaria* (Vittariaceae) in habit, leaf shape (Fig. 10–2A),
texture, venation, and the details of the spore case arrangement in long deep
grooves. In Fiji (Fig. 10–2C,D), we find another example so confusing that
practically every large herbarium in the world has misidentified the two species.

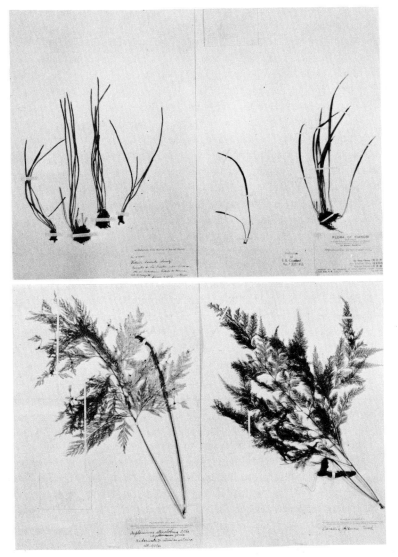

FIG. 10–2. Parallel evolution. Top: (A) *Vittaria* (Vittariaceae) vs. (B) *Drymotaenium* (Polypodiaceae). Bottom: (C) *Asplenium stenolobum* (Aspleniaceae) vs. (D) *Davallia solida* var. *feejeensis* (Davalliaceae).

One of the species, *Loxoscaphe gibberosum*, "mimics" the other, *Davallia solida*, in habitat, stem and leaf shape, the form of the sori, the length of the spore-case stalk, and so on, but the plants, as judged on other characteristics, belong to separate families (Aspleniaceae and Davalliaceae). The point is that careful and detailed studies of the plants will show that, even though numerous, their resemblances are in the minority, and that other characteristics prevail and show the true differences between the plants.

These examples of parallelism in ferns and many others like them may seem discouraging. In fact, one may wonder whether plants may actually become so alike along separate evolutionary lines that we could have "polyphyletic" genera or even species. Ownbey and Aase of Washington State University have grappled to some extent with this problem, and they point out the improbability of a series of correlated resemblances coming about by any mechanism other than a common ancestry. It is statistically very unlikely that *most* or *all* of the characteristics that are alike between two similar plants could come about by parallel evolution. This emphasizes that in the study of evolution we are dealing with probabilities. All of our methodology should be focused on improving our conclusions so that they become more and more probable. The job of the evolutionist is to determine what are the *most probable* mechanisms and pathways, and to reject the *most improbable*.

As if parallelism may not complicate the picture enough, the ferns have also been subject to *reticulate patterns* of evolution. Many of the "kinds" of ferns are actually interspecific or intergeneric hybrids that reproduce in various ways. This fact has been established beyond question during the past decade for a number of well-known species. It is possible, indeed, that as many as 10 or 15 percent of our species arose by this process of evolution. Many of the species of ferns are capable of making natural hybrids when they grow near each other. Some of these hybrids, by devices that I shall mention later, become fertile or at least can reproduce themselves. The hybrids in this way may become important members of the plant community and establish large populations.

As one would expect, fern hybrids and their derivative species are intermediate between the parents. How do we conclude that species that arise by hybridization are not in reality merely the persistent ancestors of the supposed parents? Again we deal in probabilities. Generally most features of fern hybrids "blend" the characteristics of their parents. (Rarely there is dominance, so that the hybrid may look like one or the other parent.) If it is generally true that species of hybrid origin are intermediate in their characteristics, and if we accept the idea of divergent evolution proceeding at different rates and involving different characteristics, then it is very unlikely indeed that a truly ancestral fern would lie exactly intermediate. This is diagrammed in Fig. 10–3, which shows the divergence of two lines from a common ancestor and the production of an intermediate hybrid. The common ancestor will not be an intermediate.

TIME, SPACE, AND EVOLUTION

It is essential to emphasize these concepts because commonly writers and researchers have failed to recognize them. One of the most troublesome pitfalls is the assumption that a fossil is more evolutionarily primitive than a living

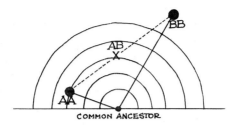

FIG. 10–3. Difference between ancestral type from which evolution proceeds at different rates and in different directions, and the intermediate condition of a hybrid species that arises by reticulate evolution.

plant. Highly specialized, highly derivative types of plants have existed at many time levels. A fern existing on the earth today may be much more primitive genetically than one that existed in the Carboniferous. The reason for this is simply that evolutionary rates differ—some lines change rapidly, and others change slowly—and divergences have occurred at all times.

If we agree that evolution is biological change—its amount, direction, and sequence—then there are two questions:

1. What are the data, the evidences? This entails the actual organisms—whether fossil or living.
2. How are the organisms connected by changes? This involves the processes by which the leaves, for example, attained their different forms, and the reproductive parts became modified.

So the study of evolutionary patterns involves actual organisms and works out the changes by which they came into being. It is important to realize as suggested above that evolution per se does not correspond to number of generations, because in some lines there might be millions of generations but little or no change, while in others the same number of generations would involve drastic changes in the populations.

This means that the question of when—when did this group of ferns evolve?—does not correspond to the actual degree of evolution. One group may have diverged very slightly several hundred million years ago, while another may have diverged radically only fifty million years ago and undergone much more extensive evolutionary change. What this means in actual research practice is that the evolutionist must study all of the diversity available without reference to chronological time. The true *race history* or what is commonly called "phylogeny," then, will give a different pattern than that of evolution. Race history can be regarded as the actual genealogy of populations through time, and that is what plant geologists or paleobotanists are primarily concerned with. Actual time or chronology is not the only problem in race history, of course, because plant populations have also migrated across the earth's surface ever since they came into being. The plant geographer, like the plant geologist, is interested in the distribution of populations, but his interest is in the history of the plant populations in relation to space rather than time. Before either the temporal or spatial history of any race of organisms can be determined, it is necessary for the systematic botanist to establish the evolutionary relationships upon which all other genealogical deductions must, of necessity, be based.

To take a simple case, the evolutionist, using his methods of correlation, establishes that the genus *Osmunda* of royal-ferns is a primitive one. The paleobotanist, then, using studies of geological deposits, establishes that this primitive fern type existed in the Carboniferous. The plant geographer, in his work, shows that *Osmunda* has had certain distribution patterns and migration routes. Thus the most complete statement of race history that we could make would answer four questions:

1. What? (What are the actual organisms from all time levels?)
2. How? (How have they changed? How much, in what directions— that is, in what characters, and in what sequence?)
3. When? (When did the changes occur, and how long, how many generations did they take?)
4. Where? (In what parts of the world, and along what migration routes?)

But it should be evident from what has been said here that our primary questions deal strictly with the evolutionary pattern itself. The questions of when and where are secondary.

DETERMINATION OF EVOLUTIONARY PATTERNS

The theory and methodology of assessing relationships of organisms is a currently lively field, and there are promises of major new advancements. The advent of the electronic computer in recent years makes it more and more likely that we shall be able to put our work on a more quantitative basis. Computer methods are just now being applied to ferns; but in ferns as well as other organisms it is a central question of just how the computer should be used. It makes no sense to use statistical or computer methods unless we have a clear idea of what we are quantifying and why. There is currently a strong cleavage of viewpoint between the so-called "numerical taxonomists" and the "evolutionary taxonomists." The numerical taxonomists argue that in working out classification all characters have equal value. This is the "Adansonianist" philosophy developed by the botanist Michel Adanson two centuries ago. The essence of the numerical methodology is to determine similarity between organisms and express it in terms of coefficients of similarity. This results in diagrams of similarity coefficients that make it possible to say that species A and species B are 90 percent alike, while species A and species C are only 75 percent alike. Obviously, any system based upon equalizing all characters is likely to meet with controversy from evolutionists. The problem of parallelisms, mentioned earlier, is one of the chief drawbacks of Adansonianism. Another is reticulate evolution. But in fairness it should be emphasized that the numerical taxonomists are not concerned with evolution. They freely admit that their work is aimed merely at assortment—a regularized, quantitative, repeatable assortment of organisms.

The evolutionary taxonomists, on the contrary, *are concerned* with patterns of relationship, and these can be determined only by careful biological analysis and correlation. The evolutionist finds that some similar characteristics are most probably due to parallelism, some are due to hybridization, and some characteristics are highly fluctuating ones that vary more or less without pattern. In ferns, for example, the thickness of the cuticle of the leaf or the leathery texture of a leaf seems to vary randomly, and practically every large genus has forms with membranous leaves and forms with leathery leaves. Hairiness of mature leaves is another of the fluctuating attributes of ferns. The evolutionist working with ferns seeks to discover what have been the changes in single characters. (For example, what have been the changes in venation patterns, in chromosomes, in spore cases, in sori, and so on?) The evolutionist also seeks to discover what have been the changes in the formation of whole organisms and of whole evolutionary lines. (For example, from what primitive stocks did the water-ferns, Marsileaceae, arise?) All evolutionary taxonomists agree that we must utilize all the biological data available, at least at the beginning. But we must be able to determine trends and patterns. Above all, we must be able to find out which characters have the greatest probability of expressing the true genetic relationships. In ferns, because of parallelism and reticulation, our picture of relationships will be badly distorted if we simply feed all comparative information into a machine without finding some way of selecting what can reliably be used. Our job is to find the threads of consistency in the irregular tangle of parallelisms, hybridizations, and fluctuating characters.

One suggested way of accomplishing this I devised some years ago, and has now been used by several researchers on ferns (Blasdell on *Cystopteris,* 1962; Brown on *Woodsia,* 1958; Mickel on *Anemia,* 1962) as well as on other plants. It is also a useful laboratory teaching device, as adapted to local availability of materials, for illustrating the methodology of evolutionary taxonomy. It comprises three steps—assortment, systematic analysis, and systematic synthesis. The method may be briefly summarized here.

Stage I: The plants are assorted and classified into groups. Usually in ferns we have a classification already available, sometimes several. If no classification has been made, a numerical-taxonomic one can be made. In any event, the preliminary assortment, whether by existing classifications or by a newly constructed one, is regarded merely as the experimental hypothesis.

Stage II: The characters are analyzed for reliability, so that those that show no pattern can be rejected and those that have definite patterns can be used. A character-state found in *all* members of a group is most probably that which existed in its immediate ancestor, but this is a "null" character and admits, of course, to no pattern. A character-state found in *most* members of a group is probably also primitive and not specialized, but this needs to be checked by outside evidence. The in-group comparison must be confirmed by comparison outside of the group with other groups of the same level and sphere of relationship. Thus the stipules or wings at the leaf bases of Osmundaceae are unusual and rare in Filicales. But outside comparison with Ophioglossales, Marattiales, other orders of ferns, and with Cycadales, the nearest order of seed plants, shows that possession of petiolar wings is the generalized, and therefore the most probable, primitive state. The character itself, however, needs study. For example, homology must be true or conclusions will be false. Homology can be tested in various ways, by studying teratologies (monstrous development) and ontogenies (normal embryological development). Also, the pattern of the character itself may be such that its changes can be deduced with high likelihood. This means that where ferns have vessels, those vessel cells that are most similar to tracheids are more primitive than those that are sharply different. In addition, there is a strong tendency for primitive characters to show a positive correlation with other nonfunctionally related primitive characters, because specialized characters represent divergences and tend to arise independently in different lines of evolution; the primitive characters, on the other hand, form the groundwork or "ground plan" of most members of all lines. After exposing each character studied to as many tests as possible to determine its consistency and reliability in demonstrating trends, those characters for which there is no or little basis of judgment and which show no trends must simply be rejected. Probably the majority of these are irregular parallelisms anyway, and have no likelihood of coinciding with evolutionary development. Others, of course, may someday be shown to have definite patterns, but from the information now available we do not know what these are, and we therefore are limited to using only those patterns for which we do have a firm and highly probable basis for evaluation.

Stage III: Once we have discovered the character trends that show strongly probable patterns, then these are connected together into the inevitable pattern of evolutionary divergence by correlating clusters of changes. For all of the basic and primitive states of characters, the value O is given—that is, no change. For all of the derivative and specialized states, we give the value of 1. The reason for this is that we have no basis to give quantitative nuances to judgments of the value of a character. Is the divided state of a leaf more than the formation of a network in venation? Until we actually know the genetic nature of characters, any attempt to give actual, graded values would be highly subjective. Only, in fact, when we have intermediate states—such as *free, casually anastomosing,* and *wholly anastomosing* veins in the leaf—can we grade values and use, say, a value of 0.5 for the in-between state.

All of the information is brought together in a table of characters and taxa (as shown in Fig. 10–4). The arrangement of the taxa, then, is based upon position in relation to the number of changes that have occurred (specialization or divergence index) and the pattern of the changes. Two species or genera

CHARACTER \ TAXON	SPECIALIZATIONS IN DIELLIA				
	UNISORA	FALCATA	MANNII	ERECTA	PREDICTED
A. Sorus dorsal to marginal.	1	1	1	1	O
B. Leaflet simple to divided.	O	O	1	O	O
C. Size moderate to dwarfed.	1	O	O	O	O
D. Veins free to all reticulate.	O	1	O	O	O
E. Midrib nearly naked to scaly.	O	1	O	O	O
DIVERGENCE INDEX	2	3	2	1	O

FIG. 10–4. Table of divergences in a genus of ferns, *Diellia*. 0 = generalized state; 1 = specialized state. See Fig. 10–7 for a correlation of these data into a diagram of the most probable evolutionary pattern.

that share character specializations A, B, and C, for example, are connected in this way with a most probable common ancestor having those attributes. One of the taxa may have become specialized further in characters D and E, while the other changed in characters F, G, and H. The former has a divergence index of 5 while the latter has evolved further, and has a d. i. of 6. Figure 10–7 shows a simple evolutionary pattern in the genus *Diellia*.

The advantages of a method such as this are the following: It forces us to examine critically all of the available data. It rejects questionable characters that do not tie together lines but represent merely parallel and fluctuating changes. If carried out carefully it should show the most probable evolutionary pattern. And, above all, it "puts the cards on the table"; all the information is shown. The bases of judgment still remain, even on the final diagram of divergence patterns. This method endeavors to consider all of the various doctrines that have been established by evolutionary biologists for the solution of systematic relationships.

ORIGIN OF FERNS

With this background of broad questions and generalizations, let us examine some special concrete problems that involve fern evolution. One of the chief problems regarding ferns, of course, has to do with their origin. From what plants were ferns, as we know them now, first derived? What were the most primitive ferns? Unfortunately the modern work gives us no reliable answer. In many ways the origin of the ferns seems to become hazier and hazier. The more than we learn about Devonian plants, where the origins of ferns are usually sought, the further we seem to get away from logical ancestral types. The Devonian plant held confidently for so many years to be a true fern— *Archeopteris*—now seems to belong to a wholly different group of plants. Of other Devonian plants, the so-called *Protopteridium* might or might not be in the fern line, but there is very little evidence. The first really clear-cut and unquestioned ferns left their remains in the Carboniferous. They were fairly primitive types in groups that still live today, and there were several families. Of other known types of plants the most similar to ferns are the Carboniferous seedferns (pteridosperms) and the more recent cycads and their relatives; and it is probable that ferns, seedferns, and cycads had an immediate common ancestor still to be discovered. It is perhaps too much to hope that common ancestral types, like those of the primitive angiosperms studied in recent years by I. W. Bailey and his group at Harvard, may still remain somewhere on the earth today as living organisms only slightly changed.

THE SEXUAL GENERATION

Modern evolutionary botanists more and more regard an organism not as a static "thing"—usually a sporophyte—but a dynamic living system, including the whole life cycle. A plant organism, then, is like an infinitely complicated cyclical chemical reaction. Each step in the process is subject to change or evolution, and one of the most neglected phases in the early years of research in botany was, of course, the gametophyte or *n* plant. In ferns in the past couple of decades the major contributions to our knowledge of the gametophyte have been made by Alma G. Stokey and her co-worker Lenette Rogers Atkinson. Common ferns tend to have more or less circular or heart-shaped prothallia of small size, 1 to 3 mm across, with very small and simply constructed sex organs (Fig. 10–6A). The more primitive osmundas and marattias have larger, thicker gametophytes with more massive sex organs. Even these gametophytes, however, are extremely simple in organization compared to fern sporophytes. Nevertheless, simple though they are, prothallia have undergone a number of profound changes in their evolution. Among the most remarkable are those of the Ophioglossales, the *n* generation of which exists underground and is evidently utterly dependent in nature upon parasitic or symbiotic fungi that exist in their tissues. The spores are thick walled, and they apparently percolate between the soil particles until they reach the level of germination. Even more drastic changes are found, of course, in the heterosporous water ferns (Marsileaceae, Azollaceae, Salviniaceae) in which the gametophytes are so reduced that they never leave their spore cases and all of their energy comes from the parent sporophytes. Even the ordinary green gametophyte is subject to changes— in cell structure, in the development of various specialized hairs or trichomes, and in shape. The most reduced photosynthetic gametophytes are those of the genus *Schizaea* which resemble algal filaments and grow in mosses in bogs and at the bases of damp tree trunks. There is some reason to believe that there may be a correlation of gametophyte shape with habitat, in particular whether or not it occurs in deep mats of mosses and liverworts. Two fern families, the filmy ferns (Hymenophyllaceae) and shoe-string ferns (Vittariaceae, Fig. 10–2), occur with mosses in tropical countries; and their gametophytes, though not truly filamentous, are very narrow and ribbon shaped. One of the most remarkable evolutionary problems in North America involves the peculiar "*Gametophyta appalachiana*," a ribbon-like, branching fern gametophyte that exists almost throughout the Appalachian region at the bases of tree trunks and in sandstone grottoes (Fig. 10–5). It reproduces solely by clusters of cells, or

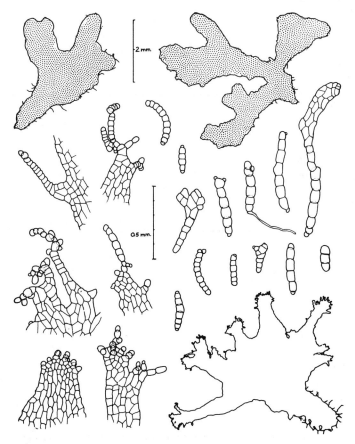

FIG. 10–5. The Appalachian gametophyte—a fern that evidently lacks a sporophyte. The shaded thalli lack marginal gemmae. The unshaded thalli and drawings with cellular details show marginal gemmae.

gemmae, which form along the margins of the prothallium, and it never produces sporophytes. Sex organs are absent or rudimentary. This may represent the most reduced of all known vascular plants. The Appalachian gametophyte has not yet been classified but it is apparently a species of shoe-string fern that has somehow lost its sporophyte in evolution. Practically all of the collections of the queer plant have been made by bryologists. In fact it was first discovered by A. J. Sharp, a bryologist who could not match it with anything known in the Bryophyta.

APOGAMY AND APOSPORY

One of the reasons that we now believe that the Appalachian gametophyte mentioned above may be a reduced stage of a shoe-string fern is that Dr. Stokey, after three years of artificially culturing the prothalium, discovered tiny young sporophytes proliferating directly from the gametophyte, and these sporophytes had certain diagnostic characteristics of the Vittariaceae. It is not often enough realized that this ability—of proliferation of sporophytes directly from the tissue of the gametophytes, without fertilization—is very widespread in ferns. In fact, I believe that we stress too much in our teaching that the alternation of chromosome number accompanying fertilization and meiosis is necessarily correlated with sporophyte-gametophyte alternation. The fact is that "alternation of generations" refers to plant bodies, not chromosome numbers. For demonstration in classes, one of the most satisfying methods is simply to take young fern leaves and put them on damp filter paper in a covered petri dish. Along the margins of the leaf, young gametophytes will grow out with the same chromosome number as the leaf, a process known as apospory (Fig. 10–6B).

During the past fifteen years new information indicates that perhaps one out of fifteen species of ferns has what is called the "apogamous life cycle," in

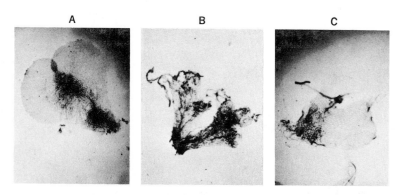

A   B   C

FIG. 10–6. (A) *Diellia* gametophyte, an "average" type. (B) Young leaf of *Pityrogramma* producing gametophytes aposporously from the margins in wet culture. (C) Apogamous gametophyte of *Pteris* showing production of the new sporophyte directly from prothallial tissue.

which both generations have the same chromosome number. The typical sexual fern cycle has reduction of chromosome number in sporogenesis; and in order to produce the new sporophyte plant, fertilization is required. In the apogamous cycle, on the contrary, the spore mother cells actually double their chromosome number by the fusion of daughter nuclei, as was worked out first by Wilhelm Döpp. One gets, therefore, a life cycle in an apogamous species with only a low number of spores per sporangium, and the doubling of chromosome number results in halving of the number of spore mother cells. An apogamous fern will thus tend to have only half the number of spores as a nearly related sexual species. Learning the cytological basis of the apogamous cycle has been a major step forward in our understanding of speciation in ferns, and the evidence seems to indicate that many if not the majority of apogamous ferns arose by hybridization or reticulate evolution. In the eastern United States our best-known apogamous ferns for teaching purposes are the narrow beech fern (*Phegopteris polypodioides*), the stiff spleenwort (*Asplenium resiliens*), and several species of cliff-brakes (*Pellaea*). In all of these—and many other species known from other parts of the world—the parent sporophyte, the gametophyte, and the new sporophyte all have the same chromosome number. The new sporophyte simply buds off of the cells of the gametophyte (Fig. 10–6C).

DIVERGENT EVOLUTION AND PREDICTION

Our methods of correlating the comparative data are improving steadily, so that more and more we shall be able to make predictions of the origins of different types of ferns. Whether we are studying problems in divergent evolution or in reticulate evolution, the goal is to be able to say with high probability what the actual pathways were and what the properties of the evolutionary ancestors were. As recent illustrations of predictive work in evolutionary research on ferns, the following will illustrate both types of patterns.

A modern monographic investigation of a group of ferns seeks not only a reasonable classification but the underlying evolutionary patterns as well. Usually the group has been troublesome and controversial to botanists, and that is why it is selected for intensive study. A number of important examples of monographic work have appeared recently, all involving the thorough examination of many characteristics—ecological, anatomical, morphological, and cytological—as well as an endeavor to correlate the multiple data into a reliable system of evolutionary relationships. Explicitly or implicitly they conclude what evolutionary origins were involved, and thus they are predictive. The Hawaiian fern genus *Diellia* is a good illustration of the approach because it involves the prediction of a common ancestor. *Diellia* was controversial because botanists, using superficial appearances and neglecting parallelisms, had placed the genus in no less than four different assemblages of ferns—groups that are now interpreted as belonging to four separate families, Pteridaceae, Aspidiaceae, Davalliaceae, and Aspleniaceae.

The types of evidence that were exploited and correlated in the research on

Diellia included ecology, the structure of the spores, the gametophyte, the gametophytic hairs or trichomes, juvenile sporophytes, rhizome, rhizome scales, pinna structure (in particular venation patterns), hairs of the frond, the ontogeny and mature structure of the sorus, the details of development and the mature form of the spore cases, and the chromosomes. Using methods like those described earlier, it was possible to extract from all these data the most probable evolutionary development of the genus (Fig. 10–7), and to state from which

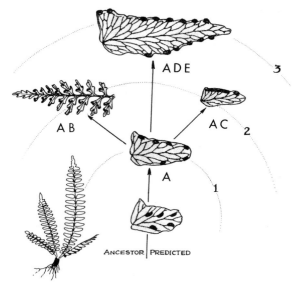

FIG. 10–7. Evolutionary pattern in the fern genus *Diellia*. Only the most divergent taxa are shown. For explanations see Fig. 10–4 and text.

family of ferns and which genus *Diellia* most likely originated. It was possible to say that evolution within the genus involved a series of divergences along several different lines away from an original *Diellia*-type that resembled— except for the orientation of the sori and the marginal veinlets associated with the specialized soral position—the ferns of the familiar "black-stemmed" spleen-worts in which the sorus occupies the entirely different medial position character-istic of the Aspleniaceae. An undiscovered ancestor was postulated—a plant that would be automatically placed in the genus *Asplenium* and related to such common ferns as ebony spleenwort, *A. platyneuron,* and maidenhair spleenwort, *A. trichomanes,* but it would differ from them in a number of features that would be divergent in the direction of *Diellia*. When the research on *Diellia* was completed, the most probable though unknown progenitor was called an "*Asplenium trichomanes* type of ancestor with dorsal sorus."

Before describing this work further, it is well to point out that the Hawaiian Islands are unusual in a number of respects, including the fact that many of the species of plants that occur there are highly localized. Furthermore, the onslaught of western civilization has been destructive to many of the native habitats. *Diellia* itself, and especially some of its species, is now a rare genus. One species, *D. mannii*, has not been re-collected since before 1900. Thus it is possible that the ancestral stock of *Diellia* does exist in the islands, or that it did exist up to the time of western destruction. After completing a monographic study of the genus in question, I was making routine identifications of ferns in the Gray Herbarium of Harvard University when I discovered a specimen named as *"Asplenium normale"*—one of the common black-stemmed spleenworts of Hawaii. However, it did not seem to fit that species superficially, and, when I examined it further, more and more differences were found. I realized then that it was not *A. normale* but another species of *Asplenium*, unknown to me, which had many features of *Diellia*. A later careful investigation, supplemented by two additional herbarium sheets found in other institutions by curators who used my drawings to select the specimens, revealed that the plant in question was to a remarkable degree the postulated ancestor of the genus *Diellia*. The total collections studied were only three, all made in 1879 on the island of Maui by F. L. Clarke. The smallest of the three specimens had been named by J. G. Baker as *Asplenium leucostegioides* in 1891 but the great Danish pteriodologist Carl Christensen interpreted that plant merely as a juvenile specimen of the common *A. normale* in 1934, and the two mature specimens had likewise been interpreted as the common species. The significance of this exceedingly rare and presumably now extinct Hawaiian plant is that its existence, past or present, had been predicted by the systematic methods of evolutionary correlation.

RETICULATE EVOLUTION AND PREDICTION

Confirmation of evolutionary predictions is less frequent in problems of divergence than in reticulation. In the latter type of evolutionary pattern, in fact, predictions of hybrids and (or) parental types have become fairly routine, thanks especially to the work of Edgar Anderson on "extrapolated correlates." Because it is generally true as indicated earlier that species characters blend in plant hybrids to form more or less perfect intermediate conditions, then careful quantitative measurements of sizes, shapes, and habitats make it possible to make predictions with considerable probability. If, for example, we have two species of plants growing together we can predict what their hybrid will look like before finding it; or, if we have one normal species and a plant that arose through hybridization of it with another species, we can tell what the other species was. Using this approach it has been possible to work out a number of evolutionary problems in the ferns, of which the Appalachian spleenworts (Fig. 10–8) are a good example.

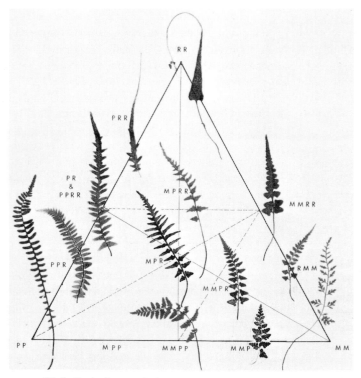

FIG. 10–8. Reticulate evolution in Appalachian spleenworts. M = *Asplenium montanum* genome; P = *A. platyneuron;* R = *Camptosorus rhizophyllus*. The hybrids with equal numbers of the basic genomes (for example, MP) are potentially or actually fertile species.

Most problems in reticulate evolution in ferns involve changes in the chromosome complements. The historical beginnings of fern chromosome study were slow and did not really start in earnest until 1950 when Irene Manton published her famous book *Problems of Cytology and Evolution in the Pteridophyta,* a landmark in the cytogenetics of ferns. Before 1950 most botanists regarded fern chromosomes as difficult because of their high numbers, especially as interpreted in microtome sections. The chromosomes could not be spread out sufficiently to be studied accurately until development of the squash technique, in which the cells are flattened under a cover slip. Cytogenetic studies of the ferns are now being made in laboratories scattered in many parts of the world (for example, D. M. Britton in Canada, Stanley Walker and Trevor Walker in England, D. E. Meyer in Germany, P. N. Mehra and his associates in India, and G. Brownlie in New Zealand), and approximately 900 different "kinds" of ferns (species, forms, hybrids) have been examined cytologically. The technique is relatively easy. Leaflets with young sori, whitish or pale-greenish, are selected and dropped into fixative and left for a few hours. Then the sporangia are scooped out with a dissecting needle and stained on a microscope slide in a drop of acetocarmine under a cover slip. As soon as they are somewhat darkened by the stain, the cover slip is pressed under the thumb or index finger, and the slide is ready for study. The technique is so simple that it can be used in teaching of botany laboratories if the appropriate microscopes with oil immersion lenses are available.

The recent studies of fern chromosomes show that the "x" or basic numbers are high; the monoploid numbers fall mostly between 25 and 50 (as compared, for example, with 6 to 11 in angiosperms). Polyploidy—the doubling, tripling, and so on of whole sets—is common. Numbers of $n = 80$ or above are not uncommon, and the highest normal chromosome complement in plants is found in an Adder's-tongue fern, *Ophioglossum petiolatum*, with a haploid number of more than 630. The base numbers in most genera of ferns are very uniform. *Asplenium* has $x = 36$; *Polypodium*, $x = 37$; *Dryopteris*, $x = 41$; *Cystopteris*, $x = 42$; and *Botrychium*, $x = 45$; but there are to be expected occasional exceptions in all of the large genera. The base numbers of chromosomes, incidentally, have been of much use in confirming ideas of divergent evolution—for example, many of the "radical" new interpretations by E. B. Copeland and R. E. Holttum of the generic relationships of ferns have been supported by the study of their x numbers of chromosomes.

Hybridity is very common in ferns, and usually shows up, if the hybrid is sterile, in irregular pairing of the chromosomes in the metaphase of meiosis. Actually, most sterile fern hybrids show no pairing of chromosomes at all. It should be pointed out too that the apogamous ferns mentioned above also show irregular pairing or no pairing, but this occurs only in those sporangia in which no doubling of the chromosome complement is encountered. What this emphasizes is that in many "cytological hybrids" pairing is only possible after doubling of the chromosome number. In the diploid state the chromosomes are sufficiently nonhomologous that the pairing mechanism is severely impaired.

The study of the Appalachian spleenworts, small cliff-inhabiting ferns of the eastern United States, revealed a complex pattern of reticulate evolution involving three wholly different original diploid parents, and the chromosomes turned out to have major importance in explaining evolution and in enabling predictions. *Asplenium* x *ebenoides,* probably the most famous of all fern hybrids, is one of the members of this complex. Its parents are the ebony spleenwort, *A. platyneuron* (Fig. 10–8, P), a common plant of rocky woods and cliffs, and the strange walking fern, *Camptosorus rhizophyllus* (Fig. 10–8, R) of mossy boulders. The hybrid, often called "Scott's spleenwort" in honor of its discoverer R. R. Scott who found it along the Schuylkill River in Philadelphia, was a source of controversy, but not because it lacked intermediacy between the parents. The hybrid indeed combined the very different shapes of the parents in a most interesting way. The controversy over its hybrid origin involved simply the fact that in one area (Hale Co., Alabama) this intermediate was not sterile, as would be expected in a cross between such widely different plants, but rather formed large, thriving populations that were entirely fertile. The botanist Margaret Slosson produced *A. x ebenoides* in artificial cultures by bringing together the parental gametophytes, and thus proved it was a hybrid. Why were the other occurrences of this intermediate fern sterile, but those in Alabama fertile? Chromosome studies showed immediately what was involved: The ordinary sterile form of Scott's spleenwort is a diploid (Fig. 10–8, PR). At meiosis there is no pairing at all; the chromosomes distribute themselves irregularly; and the spores are abortive and fail to germinate. But the Alabama type is a tetraploid (PPRR)— there are 144 somatic chromosomes, and at meiosis perfect pairing of chromosomes takes place. The Alabama Scott's spleenwort is, therefore, an amphidiploid species that has arisen from an original sterile hybrid by natural chromosome doubling. (That this can actually happen automatically was confirmed when R. L. Whitmire and I sowed thousands of spores from sterile *A. ebenoides*. A few of these spores did germinate, having double the ordinary number, and produced a new allopolyploid type.)

The origin of the fertile Scott's spleenwort was more obvious than it is with species that have arisen by hybridization but show sterile hybrids rarely or not at all in nature. The lobed spleenwort, *Asplenium pinnatifidum* (Fig. 10–8, MR), is such a species. It, like the Scott's spleenwort, lies intermediate between two species—in this case the walking-fern and the mountain spleenwort (Fig. 10–8, M), *A. montanum*. But the lobed spleenwort is so widespread and so obviously fertile that no one suspected its hybrid origin. However, both of its presumed parents have $n = 36$ chromosomes, while the lobed spleenwort has $n = 72$, exactly like fertile Scott's spleenwort. Moreover, there is an occasional sterile hybrid fern, Trudell's spleenwort (MMR), between the mountain spleenwort and lobed spleenwort. If it is true that the mountain spleenwort is one parent, then there should be pairing of certain chromosomes from lobed spleenwort with those of mountain spleenwort, and there should be, accordingly, 36 *pairs* (mountain spleenwort) and 36 *singles* (walking-fern). This is precisely what happens in the backcross hybrid, *A. x trudellii*, at the time of meiosis. (Later it was found, in much the same way, that there is homology between one of the sets of chromosomes in lobed spleenwort and the walking-fern.)

Thus, proceeding from one confirmed prediction to another, the pattern of reticulate evolution in the Appalachian spleenworts became increasingly clear. The whole picture finally formed the triangle shown in Fig. 10–8 when it was discovered that the cliff spleenwort, *A. bradleyi*, was also a tetraploid, in this case involving ebony spleenwort and mountain spleenwort. A series of checks, including detailed studies of the morphology and anatomy as well as chromosome behavior in various crosses, determined that cliff spleenwort was thus also a species that arose by reticulate evolution. The final triangle of relationships reveals a most interesting single plant—Kentucky spleenwort, *A.* x *kentuckiense,* which lies precisely in the middle of the whole complex morphologically. Remarkably, it should be possible to produce this single "kind" of fern in three different ways involving six different species: *A. montanum* x *ebenoides, A. platyneuron* x *pinnatifidum,* and *A. bradleyi* x *Camptosorus rhizophyllus.* Furthermore, this plant should be a "compound" or blend of three entirely different species. If sterile, it should have 108 unpaired chromosomes; if fertile, 108 pairs at meiosis. Unfortunately, I was unable either to produce it in culture or to find it in nature.

With good luck, Dale M. Smith of the University of Illinois and his students recently discovered a solitary plant in Kentucky of this rare fern. They brought it back to their greenhouses and grew it tenderly until it reached the proper stage for cytological study. In every respect the plant was a good intermediate between all three of the diploid "poles" of the triangle, and when it was examined cytologically at the time of meiosis the first prediction was confirmed. The chromosomes representing three different diploid species will not pair at reduction division and there are 108 singles. On the basis of this knowledge we can now predict further that there may be a fertile population of *A. kentuckiense* somewhere in the Appalachians, either at present and still undiscovered, or some time in the future.

CONCLUSION

Thus, with the two concrete illustrations given above—the problem of divergent evolution in *Diellia* and of reticulate evolution in *Asplenium*—we can conclude that it is possible to a greater or lesser extent, by refining our methods of approach and our concepts, to make predictions and to work out, with considerable probability, the actual evolutionary lines of ferns. By way of summarizing the spirit of these researches, let us ask "What are the challenges before us?" First, we must better our knowledge of the plants themselves—not merely in terms of superficial studies but with detailed analyses, including anatomical, cytogenetic, ecological, and chemical. For example, it is currently becoming evident in various laboratories that chemotaxonomic studies utilizing the chromatographic technique are capable of providing us with a whole new array of comparative facts with which to firm up our sources of evidence. Dale M. Smith and Donald Levin, for example, have recently discovered that certain chemical data on the Appalachian spleenworts coincide remarkably with the conclusions given above. Second, we must constantly improve our techniques and concepts of evaluating and correlating evolutionary patterns so that our conclusions will approach closer and closer to the actual pathways of biological changes. It is to be hoped that the study of evolution in the ferns can finally achieve the status of a predictive science, in which we can from an array of data predict kinds of plants as yet unknown, whether they exist in the past, present, or even the future.

REFERENCES

ANDERSON, E. "Introgressive Hybridization." *Biological Reviews,* Vol. 28 (1953), pp. 280–307.

BLASDELL, R. F. "A Monographic Study of the Fern *Cystopteris." Memoirs of the Torrey Botanical Club,* Vol. 29 (1963), No. 4, pp. 1–102.

BOWER, F. O. *The Ferns.* Vols. I, II, III. New York: Cambridge University Press, 1923–28.

BROWN, D. F. M. "A Monographic Study of the Fern Genus *Woodsia." Beiheftezur Nova Hedwigia,* Vol. 16 (1964), pp. 1–54, pls. 1–40.

COPELAND, E. B. "Genera *Filicum,* the Genera of Ferns." Waltham, Mass.: Chronica Botanica Co., 1947.

DOPP, W. "Die Apogamie bei *Aspidium remotum* A. Br." *Planta,* Vol. 17 (1932), pp. 86–152.

DELEVORYAS, T., ed. "Symposium on Origin and Evolution of the Ferns." *Memoirs of the Torrey Botanical Club,* Vol. 21 (1964), No. 5, pp. 1–95.

HOLTTUM, R. E. "A Revised Classification of the Leptosporangiate Ferns." *Journal of the Linnaean Society of London* (Botany), Vol. 53 (1947), No. 30, pp. 123–158.

MANTON, I. *Problems of Cytology and Evolution in the Pteridophyta.* New York: Cambridge University Press, 1950.

MICKEL, J. T. "A Monographic Study of the Fern Genus *Anemia subg. Coptophyllum." Iowa State College Journal of Science,* Vol. 36 (1962), pp. 349–482.

SMITH, D. M., T. R. BRYANT, AND D. E. TATE. "New Evidence on the Hybrid Nature of *Asplenium kentuckiense." Brittonia,* Vol. 13 (1961), pp. 289–292.

———, AND D. A. LEVIN. "A Chromatographic Study of Reticulate Evolution in the Appalachian *Asplenium* Complex." *American Journal of Botany,* Vol. 50 (1963), pp. 952–958.

STOKEY, A. G. "The Contribution by the Gametophyte to the Classification of the Homosporous Ferns." *Phytomorphology,* Vol. 1 (1951), pp. 39–58.

WAGNER, W. H. JR. "The Fern Genus *Diellia:* Its Structure, Affinities, and Taxonomy." *University of California Publications in Botany,* Vol. 26 (1952), No. 1, pp. 1–212.

———. "An *Asplenium* Prototype of the Genus *Diellia." Bulletin of the Torrey Botanical Club,* Vol. 80 (1953), pp. 76–94.

———. "Reticulate Evolution in the Appalachian Aspleniums." *Evolution,* Vol. 8 (1954), pp. 103–118.

———, AND A. J. SHARP. "A Remarkably Reduced Vascular Plant in the United States." *Science,* Vol. 142 (1963), No. 3598, pp. 1483–1484.

———, AND R. S. WHITMIRE. "Spontaneous Production of a Morphologically Distinct, Fertile Allopolyploid by a Sterile Diploid of *Asplenium ebenoides." Bulletin of the Torrey Botanical Club,* Vol. 84 (1957), No. 2, pp. 79–89.

11

Bruce Bonner

Department of Botany
University of California, Davis

In its struggle for a place in the sun, the green plant has to coordinate its growth and reproductive activities to cope with the realities of its environment. Evolution has built into plants the ability to take maximum advantage of favorable environments and to endure, avoid, or surmount unfavorable ones. One of the fascinating challenges of biology today is to understand how information about the environment is received and eventually translated into the appropriate growth responses of the plant.

Of the cues provided by the environment, probably none leads to a more interesting set of responses than does light. Nor is any of the other important factors—such as moisture, nutrients, or temperature—measured by such a specific and well-defined environmental monitoring system as the photoreceptors involved in the control of plant growth.

Phytochrome is one of these photoreceptors (light-absorbing molecules)— and a very versatile one at that, as we shall see. Through its absorption of red and far-red light and further changes it undergoes in the dark, phytochrome acts as a tuning switch in controlling many morphogenetic responses in plants. We may sometimes read the results of phytochrome control as an all-or-none effect. In other processes we measure the fine-tuning capacity—for instance, a continuously variable modulation of stem lengths between short and long extremes. In the typical all-or-none case, a response can be elicited by small doses of red light. This can be illustrated by the promotion of germination of lettuce seed that would not germinate if kept in complete darkness. However, if the red light is followed by far-red light, the initial red treatment is rendered ineffective. The promotive red effect is cancelled and most of the seeds fail to germinate. The far-red treatment prevents the previous red light from having its effect. This is the red, far-red "reversibility." This alternation of red and far-red light treatments can often be repeated a number of times with the response being determined by the last treatment given.

We have now hinted that light other than that used for photosynthesis has some importance as a set of vital cues from the environment. We can further say that we know what kind of light and when and how to give it to the plant to bring about experimentally a wide variety of responses. In the case of phytochrome we can proceed a little farther. The molecule can be taken out of the plant and can be shown to absorb specifically the light that brings about the red, far-red responses in the plant. Absorption of light does not in itself guarantee any useful subsequent event. Most of the color of flowers and some of the nongreen color of leaves is due to light absorption by pigments that do nothing more with the light than convert it to heat or send part of it back out as fluorescence. In contrast, the photosynthetic pigments trap and convert much of the light energy into chemical energy, as Lawrence Bogorad describes. Absorption of light by phytochrome, on the other hand, produces a stable change in molecule that we can measure. For our purposes we can think of this change as amounting to putting a kink in a part of the phytochrome molecule. The red, far-red reversibility is essentially putting a bend in the molecule when one packet of light energy is absorbed and straightening it out when the next packet of light (photon) is absorbed. The result of that bend is a change in the kind of light it absorbs most strongly. That is to say it changes color, and this color change resulting from light absorption can be measured in the plant itself as well as in the test tube. The pigment then exists in two forms—one absorbing red light with highest efficiency (P_R) and the other form absorbing far-red most efficiently (P_{FR}). Absorption of light by P_R converts it to P_{FR} and vice versa. This is usually written:

$$P_R \underset{\text{Far-red}}{\overset{\text{Red}}{\rightleftharpoons}} P_{FR}$$

These absorption changes are shown in Fig. 11–1.

From what we have said so far, it is clear that the form of phytochrome in the plant can be controlled by light. One form of the pigment must enter into the metabolism of the plant in such a way that many developmental processes are to a greater or lesser extent modified. At this time the precise mechanism of phytochrome action is an unknown. There is a continual accumulation of information about the relationship between light treatments and developmental processes, with a continual sorting and reevaluation of the observations in search of clues to help unravel the mystery. One of the important recent advances in plant biology was the discovery of the red, far-red reversibility, formulation of the pigment system's characteristics from physiological data, and the subsequent detection and isolation of phytochrome. These accomplishments of the group led by Sterling Hendricks and Harry Borthwick—including more recently H. W. Siegelman, R. J. Downs, and W. H. Butler—have opened the door to a far better understanding of photocontrol of plant development in all its aspects.

Red, far-red reversals are experimental manipulations to the extreme of the

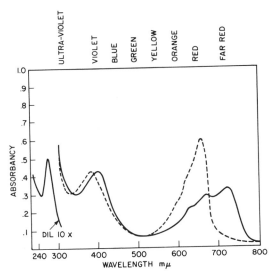

FIG. 11–1. Absorption spectrum of phytochrome from oats showing the red-absorbing form, P_R, produced by far-red irradiation (dashed line) and the far-red absorbing form, P_{FR}, produced by red irradiation (solid line). [From Siegelman and Firer, *Biochemistry, 3:* 422, 1964. Reproduced by permission of the copyright owner, the American Chemical Society.]

phytochrome pigment system. The procedure is useful in studying its properties and identifying phytochrome as the photoreceptor involved in a given response. In nature, plants are not exposed to pure red or far-red light but to a variable balance of these two portions of sunlight on the one hand and to darkness on the other. The balance of red and far-red in sunlight is most profoundly altered by passage through green leaves where the chlorophyll selectively filters out the red. Thus normal shading involves changes in light quality as well as a decrease in its quantity.

Although this blue-green molecule (the color of the light left after red has been absorbed) has been seen by perhaps a hundred or two hundred plant physiologists and visitors to four or five laboratories in the world, anyone with the slightest interest in the growth of plants can recognize the evidence of its work. Phytochrome is present in such low concentrations in plants that its color is not visible to the eye until it has been extracted and considerably concentrated. One can get a very good idea of the color by observing at night the bluish-green light of the type widely used as the go sign in traffic signals.

LIGHT AND DARK, NIGHT AND DAY

Let us consider some of those moments in the life of a plant when it is of vital importance for that plant to know it is light or dark. The seed is a good place to start. Some seeds will not germinate until after they have experienced the cold of a winter and the favorable conditions of spring have arrived. Others need only enough rain to wash an inhibitor out of their seed coat (at the same time ensuring a moist soil), or some particular temperature range or any number of combinations of external stimuli that overcome internal restraints. Many seeds—especially small ones with limited food reserves—require light for germination. A tiny lettuce seedling does not have enough food reserves to grow very much before it must produce its own food in its green leaves in sunlight. If it gets buried too deeply, it may not have the food reserves to send a shoot to the soil surface and to form a functioning leaf. Its germination may be thus delayed by the light requirement until the next time the soil is disturbed and it finds itself near the surface. Even though light requirements for germination per se are restricted, other seedling growth activities are more generally sensitive to light. They can be called de-etiolation responses—those changes resulting from the first exposure of seedlings to light. This would normally happen as the seedling emerges from the soil. In darkness the stem elongates furiously to push the leaves up to where the light should be. The leaves remain small and folded or curled, or tucked underneath a crook of the stem that normally precedes them up through the soil. Then when they receive light, the stem elongation can slow down temporarily at least while leaves are unfurled, the crook straightens out, the leaves expand, turn green, and start storing energy and carbohydrates via photosynthesis. These de-etiolation activities respond to light absorbed by phytochrome. It should be noted that the growth of plants toward unilateral illumination (phototropism) falls under control of another photoreceptor. A third pigment, protochlorophyll, is an intermediate on the pathway of chlorophyll synthesis and is thus involved in the greening process itself.

The phytochrome responsive systems just described were morphogenetic in character. We are also interested in the relationship of phytochrome to time-measuring processes that serve as the basis for the photoperiodic responses. Here the plant's course of development is responsive to day length and, thus, the season. Flowering of many plants may be elicited by the long days of spring or may be postponed to the short days of fall. To do this, a system in the leaf measures the length of the night—for example, a long night corresponds to a short day and vice versa. When the nights are of the appropriate genetically determined length for a given plant to flower, a stimulus is synthesized in the leaf and transported to the meristem at the stem tips or in lateral buds. These meristems respond by cessation of leaf formation and initiation of flowers. Phytochrome plays a role in the leaf as the main sensor of light and in some fashion controls the synthesis of this flowering stimulus. It also can play a role in the rate of flower development after its role in initiation.

This time measurement can be made with amazing precision. J. Gore studied the growth of a photoperiodically sensitive strain of rice. He grew the plants in carefully controlled day lengths and measured the flowering response in one frequently used manner—that is, the number of days before flowers (the ear) first appeared. Ear emergence occurred after 80 days on photoperiods of 11 hours and 50 minutes. Extending the days to 11 hours and 55 minutes resulted in ear emergence only after 100 days. Adding 5 more minutes per day delayed it to 120 days. The plants as a group were thus able to tell the difference between 725 and 730 minutes of darkness, which is less than 1 percent. *Xanthium* plants will show considerable increases in flowering as the night length is increased by 20 or 30 minutes in the range of 15 to 15.5 hours, and this long night exposure need be given only once. If the long nights are given three times, the differences become large. We will discuss the participation of phytochrome in such photoperiodic responses presently.

OTHER PHOTORECEPTORS

It might be well to put phytochrome in its proper place as one of several types of photoreactive systems of green plants. Much of the evidence separating out the photoreceptors involves the determination of action spectra. For a given response that can be measured in a quantitative fashion (the action) one measures the efficiency with which the various wavelengths (the spectrum) of light bring about the response. When the efficiency is plotted against the wavelength, a curve (the action spectrum) is usually obtained which can be matched with the absorption spectrum of the receptor pigment. Light is most efficient in bringing about the response when it has the highest probability of being absorbed by the photoreceptor. So red light at 665 millimicrons is most efficient in eliciting phytochrome responses because it is most efficiently absorbed by the absorption peak at 665 millimicrons. Many photobiological problems have been solved by matching the absorption spectrum of the pigment present with the action spectrum. Other problems have not been settled even with the best of data. Wnen two similarly absorbing pigments are present and the action spectrum can match either, other evidence is required to make the choice.

In the greening process, chlorophyll accumulates through a light-requiring process. Protochlorophyll in combination with a particular protein will absorb light, which causes a transfer of a pair of hydrogens to one of its double bonds, forming chlorophyll. This is a relatively straightforward photoreaction physiologically. Once the light is absorbed, chlorophyll is formed; there is no suggestion of reversal. The event occurs once for each chlorophyll *a* molecule in the plant. Chlorophyll then goes on to be incorporated into the chloroplast structure. Numerous nonflowering plants can perform the reduction of protochlorophyll to chlorophyll *a* in the dark. Common examples are many algae and pine seedlings. But in angiosperms at least, chlorophyll *a* is formed by this photochemical reaction. The precise mode of formation of chlorophyll *b* is still unclear.

The process of photosynthesis has been discussed by Dr. Bogorad in this volume. It should be apparent that as the source of energy and carbon skeletons of the plant, photosynthesis will be tied into all of the growth and biosynthetic processes mediated by other pigment systems. In practice the first thing a physiologist does in investigating some process affected by light is to devise a way to test whether or not photosynthesis is directly involved or whether the photosynthetic pigments are the light absorbers. If both answers are "no," he will usually try to eliminate photosynthesis as a variable by making it a constant, by working with a nonphotosynthetic tissue, by inhibiting the process, or by making the light quantities so small that appreciable photosynthesis does not occur. Disentangling photosynthesis from other light effects is often a real test of the ingenuity and knowledge of botany, physiology, and biochemistry for the investigator, to say nothing of the readers of the literature.

Phototropic curvatures of both higher plants and certain fungi have been extensively studied. Repeated determinations of the action spectra have resulted in the most detailed and precise data that match the absorption spectrum of a carotenoid in the visible region in the blue, but in the near ultraviolet they do not. As yet no one has been able to provide evidence acceptable to all partisans that either some carotenoid molecule or a hypothetical flavoprotein is indeed responsible.

Many of the systems responsive to the state of phytochrome can also be shown to be affected by relatively intense blue light, usually given over long periods of time. The blue irradiations sometimes produce effects quantitatively or qualitatively different from that produced by much smaller doses of red. In many of the systems, high-intensity far-red light produces the same effects as the blue. Hans Mohr in Germany has studied such responses extensively and interpreted his data to show the existence of a distinct pigment different from phytochrome and requiring higher light intensities. This is called the "high energy reaction." With the passage of time it would appear that this was to some extent a miscellaneous category. Out of it has been separated at least one system in which the photosynthetic pigments were involved. Some of the responses are due to complex effects of blue light absorbed by phytochrome. But there remains a body of evidence in favor of the existence of a photoreactive pigment absorbing mainly in the blue region.

THE TOOLS AND TRICKS OF THE PHOTOBIOLOGY TRADE

The body of knowledge concerning light and plant growth has come from many kinds of laboratories all over the world. A very important type of contribution is the description of new growth patterns or changes in a plant over which light has some fairly direct control. Finding new plants having favorable characteristics as research material is important. Photoperiodism has been studied extensively for a long time in many plants, but numerous people would like to have another good long-day plant (in addition to *Lolium temulentum*), one that will respond by flowering after exposure to one short night. The investigation of new phenomena and new plants is still vital.

At the heart of knowledge leading to advances is quantitative data relating a measurable biological response to known quantities of light under reproducible conditions. Let us illustrate what this means with respect to the study of photoperiodism in that miserable weed, the cocklebur, *Xanthium*. All over the world when people undertake photoperiodic studies, *Xanthium pennsylvanicum* is a potential choice for several reasons. It is a short-day plant that will flower after exposure to only one long night. This simplifies experiments and allows one to set up treatments that will affect various component parts of the flowering process occurring at known time intervals after the start of a long night. The seed used usually comes from that strain used by Karl Hamner and originating from the Chicago area. Local seed collections may have entirely different responses, require many more short days for flowering, be more variable in germination and growth, and in general could require much characterization work before they could be useful. In the usual experiments, one particular leaf at the same position on all plants and at the same stage of growth is chosen as the one to be given the experimental treatments. Nine days later the terminal portion of the stem is examined with a dissecting microscope and the condition of the apex is classified according to nine stages representing different degrees of flowering response. This examination of the apex allows one to circumvent secondary effects on the rate or extent of floral development. As Frank Salisbury demonstrated in his article, the floral stages do correspond to quantitative increases in the extent of induction.

The cocklebur example is no extreme of plant standardization. Even the simplest of phytochrome responding systems (lettuce seed germination) requires a particular variety of lettuce seed (Grand Rapids). Then one finds that only certain seed lots have the light requirement for germination although there are ways of treating the seed to reestablish the requirement.

In a recent study Bruce Cumming, with Hendricks and Borthwick, was investigating the relationship between phytochrome, endogenous rhythms, and photoperiodic induction of flowering in *Chenopodium rubrum*. Cumming personally examined the apices of 100,000 plants, and the investigators used a half million plants in their studies. It should come as no surprise that this particular strain from the far North can be grown 200 to a small dish, induced in the cotyledon stage by one long night when they are about five days from soaking, and the results measured a few days later using a scale similar to Salisbury's for scoring the floral stage of the apex.

The generation, control, and measurement of light in photobiological experimentation can involve anything from the simplest of techniques and equipment up through very elaborate installations. Simple fluorescent or incandescent lamps with plastic or cellophane filters can serve adequately for sources of red and far-red light. Dosages can often be varied by varying the time of irradiation within the limits imposed by the biological system. The accurate measurement of absolute light quantities requires more demanding equipment. The generation of light of one specific wavelength of good spectral purity is easily accomplished through the use of interference filters. The simultaneous provision of enough different wavelengths of adequate intensity to do an action spectrum is a formidable task. At Beltsville, to fulfill their need for a light source for action spectra, Parker, Borthwick, and Hendricks put together a spectrograph to cast a rainbow-like spectrum 6 feet wide. The light source is a very large moving-picture theatre-projector carbon arc. A huge condenser lens arrangement focuses the light and sends it through two great prisms that disperse it. Whole plants can be treated with reasonable intensities of light of narrow wave bands. More equipment is required to measure accurately the energies or absolute numbers of photons of light used in the irradiations. A plot of the quantitative response versus the light energies involved gives the action spectrum for determining what pigments are absorbing the light.

For work on phytochrome it is possible to do some spectrophotometric measurements on the pigment as it exists in the tissue. This measurement of the light-absorbing properties does require special instruments. After the pigment is extracted, it can be studied with more conventional instruments. Or, with some effort, one can grow oats in the dark, grind them up following simple directions, make a chromatographic column on which to concentrate it, and follow the little blue phytochrome band with one of the best light-sensing devices, the human eye. As it turns out, there are a number of general similarities between the rhodopsin of the eye and phytochrome.

PHYTOCHROME AND THE GROWTH OF SEEDLINGS

Seedling responses to the form of phytochrome are of special interest for several reasons. In contrast to chlorophyll-containing tissues, etiolated tissues often contain enough phytochrome and little enough interfering substances to allow spectrophotometric measurements of the relative amounts of P_R and P_{FR} in the cells. This is of some potential use in attempting to correlate the degree of physiological response with the state of the pigment. The initial absence of the photosynthetic system allows simplified interpretations about what possible photoreactive systems are involved. Etiolated seedlings make good experimental material because they can be better standardized than can material in the average greenhouse or growth chamber.

Seedlings are capable of rapid responses, and this is important for cutting down the number of links in the chain of reactions between irradiation and measurement of the response. There are a number of biochemical changes measurable in a fairly short time after light treatments, and these are being investigated to see what information about phytochrome action they might reveal.

After the discovery of red, far-red reversibility and the realization that with simple light sources one could establish the identity of at least this photoreceptor, many systems were tested for the involvement of phytochrome. As the results poured in, the ubiquitous nature of the pigment was conceded. But many experiments could not be satisfactorily explained with the restricted information available at that time. One frequently finds in a comparison of dark-grown, high-intensity white light and low-intensity red light treated seedlings that the red treatments go only part way and do not substitute for white light. Further investigation often shows that greater doses are needed and many responses are time dependent. One cannot saturate all the light response in one treatment, but continuous or periodic high-intensity radiation is required. Determinations of the action spectrum in such cases have shown a very active response to blue light that is often accompanied by a far-red peak. The energies involved are much higher than that required to convert phytochrome with red and far-red light. Hendricks and co-workers postulated a high-energy reaction (HER) with its own photoreceptor. Hans Mohr in Germany continued such studies, and with his students went on to show that both phytochrome and the HER affected the same list of reactions in white mustard seedlings. Table 11–1 lists the more important of these.

TABLE 11–1. Responses of the white mustard seedling to red, far-red, and blue light*

Straightening out of the recurved stem tip
Inhibition of hypocotyl elongation
Enlargement of the cotyledons
Formation of hairs on the epidermis of the hypocotyl
Synthesis of anthocyanin pigments

---

* From Hans Mohr, *Annual Review of Plant Physiology*, Vol. 13, 1962.

The task of separating that portion of the growth response due to phytochrome and that due to HER was approached by elaborate irradiation schemes in which the amount of red light was increased to the point where it gave no more response. Then the effect of added blue was attributed to the HER. Mohr's group has recently taken into account the fact that phytochrome does absorb blue light, that blue of adequate intensity will set a balance between the two forms of phytochrome, and that the far-red peak in the HER is most likely due to phytochrome. The result is that a portion of HER reactions are now being assigned to the effects of long-term high irradiations of phytochrome. There is much more to learn about the results of such treatments on the concentration of P_{FR}.

It does not take much consideration of the problem to see that if one carries the formal criterion of red, far-red reversibility to the extreme, one can relate almost everything to phytochrome. By comparing a dark-grown to a red-irradiated seedling, one could argue that the uptake of water is promoted by phytochrome P_{FR} in the leaf and inhibited by P_{FR} in many stems. Certainly leaf expansion involves water uptake and the inhibition of stem elongation would involve the lessening of water uptake. Since a plant grows differently in light and darkness, one can measure any number of constituents or properties and find that they differ from light- to dark-grown material. How does one tell which are more closely related to the primary site or sites where phytochrome gets involved with cellular metabolism? If we had a really good answer for this question this article would be explaining the mechanism of action of phytochrome. One of the more comforting approaches is to put one's faith in kinetics. We can assume that the closer in time we approach the initial formation of P_{FR}, the nearer any changes we measure will be to P_{FR} action. Those people in the group with William Klein have followed some events in corn seedlings that are phytochrome controlled. In the dark the first leaf is tightly rolled up into a tube form. By twelve hours after a red flash of a few seconds duration, the leaf has visibly started to unfurl. This is a phenomenon previously shown in other grasses. But prior to the unfurling, they find a breakdown in starch and decline in sugars in the tissue which is measurable after three hours. The question remains as to whether changes in carbohydrate metabolism brought about growth changes or whether some early demands of the growing cells upon the carbohydrate reserves resulted in the decrease in starch and sugar rather indirectly. James Lockhart has shown that measurable changes in the physical properties of pea stems do occur within an hour after irradiation (presumably acting through phytochrome). His growth measurements show that the elongation has slowed within this time. The changes in stiffness of the stems undoubtedly involve an increased deposition of cell wall material. This is just the sort of demand on carbohydrate reserves that might account for the changes described in corn seedlings above. There are definite changes in growth rate measurable between ten and fifteen minutes after red treatment in one seedling system under investigation in our laboratory. We expect therefore that even secondary metabolic changes would occur in a very short time. The shortness of time intervals between phytochrome activation and responses so far measured does not guarantee that we are seeing a primary event controlled by phytochrome itself. It is of interest that this fifteen-minute interval between irradiation and change in growth rate is about the same as that Peter Ray observed in oat coleoptiles between the time auxin is added and the growth rate increases.

Many observations relate light inhibition of stem elongation and the promotion of elongation by gibberellins. A striking phenomenon found in numbers of plants is that reduction in stem length caused by red irradiation can be overcome by the application of gibberellins. This is especially true of dwarf strains. These tend toward normal development in darkness while their dwarf character is expressed strongly in light. It was proposed that light inhibits the synthesis of the gibberellins, resulting in shortened plants. Applying the hormone to the plant more or less restores the tall configuration. More recent results indicate that perhaps gibberellin may not be needed for etiolated growth. Light appears more likely to influence the sensitivity of tissue toward certain of the dozen different gibberellin forms. Certainly the results most difficult to reconcile with any simple direct relationship between phytochrome and gibberellins are those with wheat coleoptiles in Alan Haber's laboratory. When the coleoptiles were about an inch high, they were marked to divide them into three parts. The effect of red light (far-red reversible) was to cause the upper third to elongate more than in the dark. The middle thirds were about equal. The basal portion was inhibited by red. When gibberellin was applied, it promoted the growth of all three portions of the red-treated coleoptile so that in the lower portion it was counteracting the effect of red irradiation. In the apical portion, red and gibberellin were acting in the same direction. A consistent simple relationship is not attained in the same organ, so the gibberellin and red light question remains open. Advances in relating specific gibberellins to specific responses are certain to be of great importance in untangling light and gibberellin.

PHYTOCHROME IN LIGHT-GROWN PLANTS

With all the emphasis on etiolated seedlings, an experiment of R. J. Downs should make it clear that phytochrome is there and working in light-grown material. The essence of the experiment is that the state of the pigment during the night affects the rate of stem elongation. Downs grew bean plants with high-intensity fluorescent light during the day. Then as they entered the dark period, phytochrome was pushed into either the P_R or the P_{FR} form. After a few nights of this regime the internodes were much longer in those plants given far-red at the beginning of the dark period (Fig. 11–2). It can be concluded that phytochrome P_{FR} was present at the end of the day and that it controls elongation for some part of the night. It was further demonstrated that if one gave far-red at the beginning and red in the middle of the dark period, the growth was about halfway between the extremes given by far-red and red at the beginning. If the order was reversed so that P_{FR} was present the first eight hours and P_R the second eight hours, the results were the same, so elongation is controlled in both parts of the night. The sensitivity to far-red reversal was retained through the night, and there is no indication that any change from P_{FR} to P_R ("dark-reversion") is taking place, although it cannot be excluded as occurring to an extent that did not reach limiting concentrations of P_{FR}. This type of response is widespread, although the difference between the extremes of elongation varies with the species and variety.

This phenomenon has two important probable applications. It can account for at least part of the often remarkable difference between plants grown under fluorescent light and those grown under incandescent light of the same intensity. The fluorescent lamps serve to leave phytochrome in the P_{FR} form as night begins. The incandescent lamps leave a lower concentration of P_{FR} because of their high far-red content, relatively greater than that of sunlight. In some cases the difference in height is spectacular, incandescent lamps favoring extreme elongation.

FIG. 11–2. Changes induced in internode length of pinto beans at the end of an eight-hour day. The plant on the left received no supplementary radiation, the one in the center far-red radiation for five minutes, and the one on the right far-red radiation for five minutes followed by red radiation for five minutes. [From Hendricks, in *Photophysiology*, Vol. I, ed. A. C. Giese, 1964, by permission of Academic Press. Photograph courtesy of Dr. S. B. Hendricks.]

The rate of development of the flowering stalks of grains is apparently influenced by such a phenomenon, although some people hold that high energy systems are most important.

In nature we can look at the tall spindly form that many sun-loving plants assume when growing in the more or less continuous shade of other plants. Naturally low light intensity plays an important role in the response. In addition, the light that these plants receive after filtration through the leaves above them is relatively much richer in far-red. Chlorophyll uses up the red. These shaded plants then could be expected to become maximally elongate. One could hypothesize that this might have survival advantage in hastening their emergence out of the shade into the brighter light.

LIGHT AND THE GROWTH OF WOODY PLANTS

While the experimentalist tends to favor small rapid-growing plants, and the result is an apparent association of phytochrome with such plants, there is ample evidence that the growth of trees may be controlled in several ways by the photoperiod and that they possess the red, far-red system. A simple experiment of R. J. Downs will illustrate a number of points. He gave young

Catalpa bignoniodes plants, the familiar Catalpa tree, eight hours of sunlight to provide adequate photosynthesis for normal growth. Two lots of plants were given a day-length extension of eight more hours with only 30 footcandles of either incandescent or fluorescent light, a light level that would have no significant contribution to overall photosynthesis (a bright clear day may have 10,000 footcandles of sunlight at midday). A control received no day-length extension. The results are shown in Table 11–2.

TABLE 11–2*

Kind of Supplemental Light (All Receive 8 Hours Sunlight)	Catalpa bignoniodes	
	No. of Nodes	Stem Length in Cm
None (8-hour day)	2	2.5
Incandescent filament (high in far-red)	6	20.7
Fluorescent (low in far-red)	6	10.6

* From R. J. Downs, "Photoperiodic Control of Growth and Dormancy in Woody Plants" in *The Physiology of Forest Trees,* edited by K. V. Thimann, Copyright © 1958 The Ronald Press Company.

Short days cause the cessation of stem elongation. Node and leaf formation ceases as the terminal meristem turns black and abscises. Under the long-day conditions with essentially no more light available for photosynthesis, the plants continue to grow and form new nodes. Besides the effect of short days, another effect obvious from the data shows that the red and far-red balance in the supplemental light profoundly influenced the stem elongation. This is attributable to the maintenance of different concentrations of the P_{FR} form. In this case, activity of the terminal meristem can be controlled by the photoperiod. The extent to which a given internode, once formed, elongates appears to be influenced by the ratio of red and far-red light. There are obvious similarities to stem elongation in herbaceous plants.

That the photoperiodic control is similar to the systems in control of floral initiation can be seen in R. J. Downs' experiments with Douglas fir (*Pseudotsuga menziesii*). Illustrated in Fig. 11–3 are plants grown for one year on photoperiods of twelve hours, twelve hours plus a one-hour interruption with 40 footcandles of incandescent light in the middle of the dark period, and a twenty-hour photoperiod. The inhibitory effect of the long night has been overcome by the interruption.

The precise interrelationship between organ formation and stem elongation is not yet clear. The activities of leaves are important in determining the behavior of the apical meristem so the leaf may be the site of the photoreceptor as far as the effect on leaf or node formation. It is most likely that the pigment existing in cells of the stem at the time of rapid elongation is most influential in modulat-

FIG. 11–3. Growth of Douglas fir [*Pseudotsuga menziesii* (Mirb.) Franco] after twelve months on (left to right) photoperiods of twelve hours, twelve hours plus a one-hour interruption near the middle of the dark period, and twenty hours. [From R. J. Downs, "Photocontrol of Growth and Dormancy in Woody Plants" in *Tree Growth,* edited by T. T. Kozlowski, Copyright © 1962 The Ronald Press Company; courtesy of U.S. Department of Agriculture.]

ing stem elongation in response to the ratio of red and far-red light. These sorts of effects have been demonstrated in many woody plants, even those of tropical origin. For any species, the extent to which such responses are manifested is determined by a host of factors built into the genetic constitution of the plant, by its particular environment and by such things as the amount of carbohydrate stored in the previous season. Just what photoperiods will permit elongation appear to be associated with those photoperiods in which the plant could grow and survive in its native habitat. There is evidence that a series of collections of trees of one species can respond to quite different photoperiods, depending upon the latitude of their origin. The farther from the equator the place of origin, the longer days they would normally get during the growing season and the longer the days must be to prevent them from going dormant, other factors being constant. Some evidence indicates that, for a given latitude, plants from higher elevations, where favorable temperatures prevail for a shorter time, will cease growth earlier in the season. One can say as a generalization that a population of plants in its native habitat tends to be fairly precisely tuned into its environment. The photoperiod is frequently the most reliable indicator of the progress of the seasons, and through evolution the particular length of photoperiod assuring survival and maximum competitive advantage has been selected for triggering the onset of dormancy in buds and even the breaking of dormancy in the spring in some species. On the other hand some plants go dormant even under continuous light without being influenced by the photoperiod.

LOWER PLANTS

Phytochrome is now known to occur in a number of lower plant groups. Fern sporeling elongation, fern and moss spore germination, and the orientation of chloroplasts in certain green algae have been demonstrated to respond to red and far-red treatments just as do higher plants. The chloroplast in the algae *Mougeotia* and *Mesotaenium* is a strap-shaped structure generally running nearly the length of the cell. It is wide and flat so that looking at it from one edge of the cell it appears thin. From the top it would look wide. These chloroplasts rotate on their long axis within a stationary cell so as to intercept either a maximum or a minimum amount of light. Under bright light the edge is turned to the light, while in low intensities the wide face is turned to intercept the maximum amount of light. W. Haupt in Germany clearly demonstrated that the orientation in response to low intensities is controlled by red light. Far-red reverses red effects. This is one of the most rapid physiological responses in that it takes about thirty minutes. Haupt has shown in a fascinating set of experiments with polarized light that the phytochrome is localized in a thin layer around the surface of the cytoplasm. The potential utility of single cell organisms for biochemical investigations led us to attempt to find phytochrome in *Mesotaenium*. A. O. Taylor and I have separated phytochrome from the fully green cells. The quantity extracted is low compared with that in an etiolated pea seedling, for instance, but it has interesting properties. It has the same reversibility but the absorption peaks are different from the classical higher plant type. The maxima are both shifted about 15 to 17 millimicrons to the shorter wavelengths. It is of interest from a comparative biochemistry view to know whether the protein or the chromophore or both are different from the higher plant form. It also reminds us that there may well be significant variants among higher plants. We have no idea of the distribution of the pigment among the algae in general. Where else will it turn up?

PHYTOCHROME AND THE PHOTOPERIODIC CONTROL OF FLOWERING

Among the world's plants there exists a wide variety of behavior patterns associated with those reproductive activities involving initiation and development of flowers. These patterns vary among perennial, biennial, and annual plants, tropical and temperate, and even from one genotype to another in the same species. The patterns of reproductive behavior we assume to have been selected through the course of evolution to allow survival in the particular habitat of the species or ecotype. It seems that the precise course of development of a plant generally is not predetermined, but rather the plant is endowed with predetermined patterns of development that are triggered or modulated by environmental factors. In one selection of a species it might be most advantageous to initiate reproductive activity in response to rain or to a period of cold weather or to the season. While temperature, moisture, and other factors may be reliable enough to serve as cues for some plants in certain habitats, the changing length of the day and night serves many plants as a very reliable cue from the environment around which to build a pattern of vegetative and reproductive activities assuring survival. The regular advance of longer days in the spring and shorter days in the fall is surely far more reliable than temperature or moisture in many habitats. The lengths of the light and dark periods are much more reliable than is the total quantity of light received by the plant. The quantity of light will vary tremendously with variable cloud cover, fog, shading by other plants or objects, reflections from surrounding surfaces, etc. It seems appropriate that a successful cue from the environment might simply tell the plant to the first approximation whether it is light or dark. To the best of our knowledge the phytochrome system is the only light receptor hooked into the metabolic machinery of the plant in such a way as to monitor the environment for the light versus dark situation. Phytochrome can and does do more than this, but for the photoperiodic system under natural conditions this is the essential cue. The light or daytime condition results in the conversion of P_R to P_{FR} to an extent such that a metabolically effective level of P_{FR} is attained. This level can be attained at intensities of light somewhere between that of twilight and of the full moon.

This monitoring system must be hooked into a time-measuring system for the plant to respond to the day or night length. The mechanism involved in this time measurement is one of the most fascinating problems in plant physiology. It also has its controversies. In her article, Beatrice Sweeney has described how circadian rhythms are manifested in a variety of processes in plants. She has conveyed many of the ideas about the existence of and properties of the biological clock. Many people believe that time measurement in the photoperiodic responses involves the biological clock. Many others hold that the measurement of night length in photoperiodic systems is separate under natural conditions, but that under the long or abnormal cycles of light and darkness used for the study of endogenous rhythms complicated interactions between the biological clock and the photoperiodic timing system can occur, obscuring the basic independence of the two systems. The field is an active one at present, and we look forward to a resolution of the role of biological clocks in photoperiodism.

GENERALIZATIONS

The leaves are the principle sites of time measurement under most situations. This has been shown for both long- and short-day plants by exposing the leaves or a single leaf to an inductive photoperiod while keeping the buds in which the flowers are initiated on a noninductive photoperiod.

The length of the night, the dark period, is more important than the day length in controlling flowering. Interruption of a favorable light period with a short period of darkness generally has no effect on the flowering. On the other hand, interruption of an inductive long night with a short-light treatment will prevent that dark period from promoting flowering in a short-day plant. If long-day plants are maintained on nights longer than the critical period, they will not ordinarily flower. But interruption of that night with a short-light treatment can promote the flowering response. The length of the uninterrupted dark period is the determining factor. Further, it is well documented that the light effective in interrupting the night is the light that converts P_R to P_{FR}. Action spectra for night interruptions of both long- and short-day plants fit the absorption spectrum of P_R. Nullification of the red effect by far-red treatments clinched the identification of phytochrome. If a light treatment produces P_{FR} in the dark period, the reversal with far-red treatments clinched the identification of phytochrome. If a light treatment produces P_{FR} in the dark period, the reversal with far-red can be performed if the far-red is given soon enough. In the case of *Xanthium*, R. J. Downs has shown that the effectiveness of far-red in negating a red interruption progressively declines to zero in about thirty-five minutes. This "escape from photocontrol" is interpreted as a manifestation of the functioning of P_{FR} after its formation. Eventually it will have catalyzed enough of its hypothetical reaction so that the inhibitory function is completed, and converting it back to P_R no longer makes any difference. In the interesting case of *Pharbitis nil*, the Japanese morning glory, H. Fredericq has recently shown that the presence of P_{FR} for much more than thirty seconds will interrupt an otherwise inductive night. Far-red reversals must be started within thirty seconds after a red-light interruption in order to be effective in preventing too much of the inhibitory reaction from occurring.

Thus, during a longer than critical dark period a process goes on in the leaves favoring floral induction in short-day plants and inhibiting it in long-day plants. How is the message transmitted from the leaf to the potential flower bud on the stem of the plant? The best evidence says that it is a chemical stimulus made in the leaf accumulating to effective levels in short-day plants as the night surpasses the critical length. The Russian botanist Chailakhyan classed the stimulus as a flowering hormone and named it "florigen" in 1937.

In the case of *Xanthium* it can be shown that effective amounts of stimulus move out of a single induced leaf after about twenty hours from the beginning of an inductive dark period. This is determined by removing the induced leaves from successive groups of plants at various times after the start of the inductive night. The stimulus continues to move for perhaps twelve to twenty-four hours in the short-day plant *Xanthium* as evidenced by progressively greater flowering response the longer the induced leaf is left on. Stages of development of the young flower bud showing increasing intensity of floral induction are shown in Fig. 11–4. It has also been shown that the stimulus moves in the phloem after

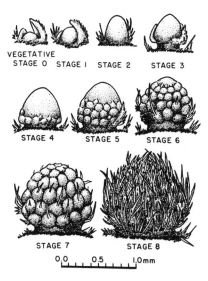

FIG. 11–4. Stages of development of a male flower bud axis in *Xanthium* about nine days after beginning short-day treatments. These represent increasing degrees of induction. [From F. B. Salisbury, *Plant Physiology, 30:* 328,1955. Reproduced by permission.]

leaving the leaf blade since various girdling treatments to the petiole and stem prevent its movement. This idea is corroborated by experiments in which the movement of the products of photosynthesis is manipulated. If an actively photosynthesizing leaf is interposed between the induced leaf and the bud, it can prevent the subsequent flowering. Application of radioactive carbon dioxide to the induced or noninduced leaves confirms the idea that when the translocation of photosynthates pushes the products of the induced leaf away from the bud, flowering does not occur. If the photosynthate from the induced leaf moves to the bud, flowering can follow.

In the long-day plant, the grass *Lolium temulentum,* one sufficiently long-light period will allow the synthesis of a factor that moves out of the leaf and to the bud in much the same way as in the short-day plants. There is evidence for some inhibitory effect moving from noninduced leaves. Substances inhibitory to flowering have been demonstrated in some systems. Their real significance in photoperiodism as a whole is not clear.

Is the "florigen" of short-day plants the same as that of long-day plants? What about day-neutral plants? There is a series of experiments addressed toward these questions carried on by M. Chailakhyan, F. Melchers and A. Land, Jan Zeevaart, and others. Their methods have involved the grafting of pairs of plants to give them combinations of two photoperiodic response classes. The grafted pair was maintained under conditions normally allowing one to flower but not the other. In a sizable number of cases the induction of one plant results in the flowering of both. If a long-day donor such as *Hyoscyamus niger* is grafted to a short-day Mammoth tobacco plant and the pair are kept under long days, the tobacco will flower even though a control tobacco kept under the same conditions will remain vegetative. Using a variety of combinations has led to the conclusion that the "florigen" of long-day, short-day, and day-neutral plants is the same in the various plant types. These response types differ with respect to the presence or absence of the hormone under given photoperiodic conditions.

Many laboratories have attempted to extract florigen and apply it to plants under noninductive conditions to cause flowering. Some encouraging preliminary results of Lincoln, Mayfield, and Cunningham using extracts of *Xanthium* have not been followed with all the success for which one might have hoped. The relationship of their extracts to florigen is yet to be clarified. On the other hand the gibberellins may be applied to many rosette-form long-day plants causing rapid elongation of the stem and flower formation. Gibberellins then could fit the criterion required of florigen for many rosette-type long-day plants. But they do not cause flowering in short-day plants or caulescent long-day plants. So if the conclusion from the grafting experiments is right, that florigen is essentially the same in long-day, short-day, and day-neutral plants, gibberellins are not the same as florigen. Jan Zeevaart and Anton Lang have made ingenious use of *Bryophyllum daigremontianum,* a long–short-day plant. It requires a period of long days followed by a period of short days in order to flower. They showed that the long-day requirement could be satisfied by applied gibberellin in short days, but that synthesis of a transmissible floral stimulus, florigen, requires short days irrespective of the manner in which the long-day requirement is met. They did this by grafting scions onto stocks (receivers onto donors). In order for the donor to cause a receiver to flower, the donor must have been exposed to short days following long days or gibberellin treatment. Having had such treatment the donor stock is an effective inducer no matter whether the receiver is on long or short days. An attractive interpretation of these results is that gibberellin may be the "physiological precursor" of florigen. Many workers are convinced that the relationship between gibberellins and florigen is a close and direct one. There are stimulatory effects of gibberellins on flowering in short-day plants. These would appear to be more connected with the expression of flowering, the processes taking place in the stem. As Anton Lang emphasizes, gibberellins may carry on different functions associated with different sites of action.

PHYSIOLOGY OF PHYTOCHROME

The function of the protein phytochrome is entirely unknown at present. Suggestions that it functions in some aspect of acetate metabolism are only speculative. The fact that it is present in low concentrations coupled with the estimation that only a very small percentage conversion to P_{FR} will elicit a fundamental change in the growth indicates that P_{FR} must function catalytically. In etiolated pea seedlings the total concentration is of the order of 3×10^{-6} Molar or perhaps 0.03 percent of the fresh weight. This is the region of the stem with the smallest cells, where the vacuoles occupy less of the cell volume and protein concentration is highest. As one drops down away from the apical region and the cells have elongated to the maximum, the pigment concentration per unit of fresh weight is very much lower. In the several etiolated seedlings investigated, the concentration is roughly proportional to total protein concentration.

The most surprising discovery concerning phytochrome came out of the early experiments of H. W. Siegelman. He found that the yields of extractable phytochrome declined drastically when the seedlings were exposed to light. The effective light was shown to be that absorbed by phytochrome itself. Ultimately it was shown that once P_{FR} is formed it starts to "decay" to some form that does not respond to far-red light. This decay product has yet to be identified. Within three to five hours of formation, P_{FR} has dropped to an undetectable level in those etiolated seedlings investigated, and this seems to be the rule in etiolated materials. This is illustrated by the P_{FR} (P_{730}) curve in Fig. 11–5. This reaction is stopped by holding the plants near freezing and can be slowed by applying certain respiratory inhibitors. In a few plant tissues, P_{FR} is apparently stable to this decay system. In these tissues there is a slow reversion of P_{FR} to the P_R form in the dark.

The physiological significance of this decay of P_{FR} is not yet clear. It could be an expression of some mechanism for regulating the concentration of phytochrome and so set up as to maximize the pigment concentration in darkness. There is also the formal possibility that P_{FR} is not active in itself but must undergo the decay reaction before it can function. In any of the systems so far studied it is easy to fit such a concept into the available data as an alternative to the more generally accepted idea that P_{FR} itself is active. Whatever the final answer to that problem, the changing total concentration of pigment after an initial P_{FR}-producing irradiation is an important factor to consider in interpreting many physiological experiments. With continuous red irradiation, one could expect to deplete entirely the store of measurable phytochrome in a mat-

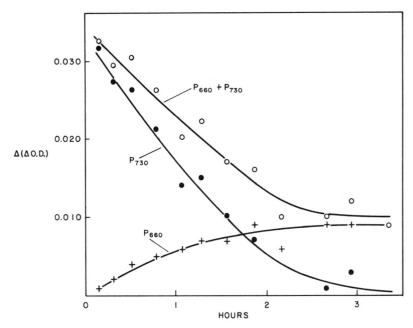

FIG. 11–5. The changes in phytochrome concentration after red irradiation of seven-day-old corn seedlings. The measurements are of phytochrome in the cells. The P_{730} (P_{FR}) curve shows the "decay" of P_{FR}. The P_{660} (P_R) curve shows the amount of P_R that becomes available for conversion to P_{FR} by a second red treatment as P_{FR} disappears. [From Butler, Lane and Siegelman, *Plant Physiology, 38:* 516,1963. Reproduced by permission.]

ter of some hours. On the other hand the concentration of pigment required for normal function may be so low that even under conditions of rapid decay new synthesis would provide enough P_R to supply a sufficient transitory concentration of P_{FR} to fulfill all needs. The interesting experiments of Masaki Furuya, John Torrey, and William Hillman show that a physiological response (lateral root initiation in cultured pea roots) is not responsive to the pigment form at a stage when phytochrome is easily detectable. As the time from excision from the seedling increases, spectrophotometrically detectable pigment disappears, but the lateral root initiation becomes sensitive to the state of the pigment and can be controlled by red and far-red light. This points up the difference between the study of phytochrome and the study of an enzyme for which there exists an assay of the activity. Phytochrome must be detected by its own physical properties, light absorption. An enzyme is studied by the product of its action. This can be so arranged in many cases that an enzyme produces in a few minutes many thousands of molecules as strongly light absorbing as phytochrome so the limits of detection are far lower. When and if an enzymatic reaction is found for phytochrome, one should be able to study it in tissues at far lower concentrations than are presently needed for direct light absorption.

The "photostationary state" is a term used to denote the fact that with most kinds of light absorbed by phytochrome one reaches a point beyond which further irradiation causes no net change in distribution between P_R and P_{FR}. The particular balance achieved depends upon the efficiency with which the given wavelength causes the forward and reverse transformation. Both forms of phytochrome absorb throughout the visible region. The chances of P_{FR} absorbing red light are less than those of P_R. But once absorbed, red light will convert either form to the other. One can readily see that, starting with either form, continuous irradiation will eventually bring a solution of phytochrome to the same mixture of the two forms as the rate of transformations in each direction become equal. Such an experiment (though in this case using blue light) is shown in Fig. 11–6. Blue light brings about the same mixture of P_R and P_{FR} irrespective of which form predominated initially.

In the "photostationary state" the total pigment concentration remains constant. If, however, one of the two forms is being removed (P_{FR} in the "decay"

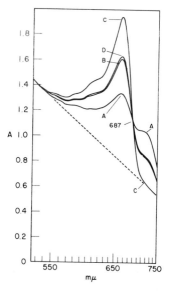

FIG. 11–6. The photostationary state of phytochrome from peas under high-intensity blue irradiation. The preparation was first irradiated with thirty seconds of red light to convert it to P_{FR} (curve A). Then a five-minute blue irradiation brought it to a mixture of P_R and P_{FR} (curve B). Next it was converted to P_R by far-red irradiation (curve C). A second blue treatment brought the pigment back to the same mixture of P_R and P_{FR} (curve D) as when starting with P_{FR}.

reaction) then the balance will be upset. If one irradiates with red to the photo-stationary state there is still 20 percent of the P_R left. When P_{FR} is subsequently removed by the decay reaction, the only remaining pigment is that 20 percent P_R. A second red irradiation will then convert some more of the P_R that was not converted the first time as illustrated in Fig. 11–5. This could be mistaken for a synthesis of P_R or a reversion of P_{FR} to P_R in the darkness and has in the past been a source of confusion.

It is easy to see from these properties of the pigment that blue light can act through phytochrome. There are well-established examples of blue light giving the same effects as red, and, further, the blue light effect is far-red reversible. In other situations the effect of blue is the same as far-red and is reversible by red. When these effects of blue light are coupled with a time- and concentration-dependent decay of P_{FR}, it is difficult to separate phytochrome responses from those of the high-energy reaction.

PHYTOCHROME IN SOLUTION

Phytochrome has been extensively purified from etiolated oats and peas. The choice of material is based upon initial high phytochrome content, low-cost seeds, and successful performance of purification steps with adequate recovery of the pigment. Barley and corn were discarded after many trials because the phytochrome was prone to denaturation or the purification proved difficult to push beyond a certain point.

Phytochrome is a large protein although its molecular weight is not finally determined. Since we know nothing of any catalytic activity as yet, most of the studies involve the light-absorbing characteristics. Proteins composed solely of amino acids do not absorb visible light appreciably, so one question concerns the identity of the group on the molecule that gives it the color (the chromophore). H. W. Siegelman has recently been able to remove the chromophore in low yield and show that it is similar to the open chain tetrapyrolle bile pigments:

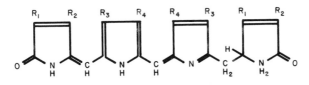

These tetrapyrolles are highly colored compounds and also constitute the chromophores of the red and blue photosynthetic pigments responsible for the characteristic colors of the red and blue-green algae. The absorption spectrum of phytochrome resembles that of one of these algal pigments, allophycocyanin. An apparent difference between phytochrome and the algal pigments is in the number of bile pigment molecules attached to one protein molecule. There is no evidence for more than one chromophore per phytochrome molecule while phycocyanins, for instance, have from twenty-two to thirty bile pigment groups per molecule.

The bile pigment molecule has isomeric forms that could account for the existence of the two forms of phytochrome. It is quite possible that the act of light absorption isomerizes the chromophore and the isomeric forms are stabilized by a tightly fitting protein to give P_R or P_{FR}. Molecules of the size of the chromophore can in addition cause changes in the shape of proteins to which they are attached. It is possible to speculate that a change in isomeric form of the chromophore induces a rearrangement of the folding of the protein to expose an active site for the hypothetical phytochrome reaction.

Most proteins are initially characterized with respect to their catalytic activity. Lacking knowledge of the latter has limited biochemical characterization of phytochrome to the effect of various reagents on its light-absorbing properties. The conclusion is that phytochrome is sensitive to reagents that interfere with hydrogen and sulfur bonds normally involved in maintaining proteins in a stable form, properly coiled and folded into a compact unit. P_{FR} is much more sensitive to these denaturing reagents, which is in keeping with the idea that P_{FR} has more groups exposed than does P_R as a result of small changes in the shape of the protein.

Some recent experiments of W. L. Butler and of Winslow Briggs and David Fork have shown that the phytochrome transformation from one form to the other is slow in the photochemical sense. It involves intermediate steps after the initial light absorption event before the stable alternative form appears. All these changes take place in fractions of seconds, so they are observed only with special equipment. They resemble the changes that occur when pigments in the eye absorb light. This further evidence is compatible with intimate involvement of the protein with the chromophore in determining the light-absorbing characteristics.

After the discovery of the basic nature of phytochrome there was a flurry of activity to test many plants and many physiological and biochemical processes for the involvement of the pigment. There was an emphasis on the description of those that are responsive. Now there is a current trend to investigation of the exceptions and an attempt to go beyond the simple experiments to bridge the gap between ten seconds of red light and ten hours of sunlight. The plants produced by treatments of this sort do not show differences as great as those grown in darkness and those grown in sunlight.

There is a long way to go in understanding all the roles of light. The solution may well involve identification of a new blue-light-absorbing pigment, and will require a much better understanding of the changes in sensitivity to light within the course of development of a cell. Obviously, a key that will unlock many doors is knowledge of the event controlled by phytochrome.